South America
Teacher/Parent Notes

The purpose of this book is to help young people become more familiar with South America through reading, writing, researching, and illustrating. They can then share the information they discover with classmates, friends, and family.

Present as much information as possible about a specific region or country before having students complete the related activity sheets. Have available encyclopedias and other reference books so that the students can accomplish the research necessary to complete the activity sheets. They may find the *World Book Encyclopedia* to be most helpful. Teachers/Parents are encouraged to add information on other locations, points of interest, rivers, and so on, when working on the mapping activities.

The following methods may be used to integrate this book into your curriculum:

Independent Activities

Each student may work on the activity sheets of his/her choice. The activity sheets can be stored in a folder. After all of the materials for a specific country have been completed, the teacher/parent should have a conference with the student to go over the materials together. If any information is incorrect, help the student locate the correct answers. The materials may then be stapled into a booklet.

Small Group Activities

The students may be divided into small groups to work on the specific countries of South America. After a group has completed the work, they may share their information with the other groups. Creative presentations should be encouraged. For example, one group may decide to present their findings through a simple play, while another group may share what they have learned through an imaginary travelogue.

Large Group Activities

You may wish to have the entire class or a large group work on certain pages, displaying the chosen pages on an overhead projector and working through the pages together.

Special Note

Advise students to remain alert to current events taking place in South America. You might maintain an ongoing bulletin board to display newspaper and magazine articles which relate to South American countries.

Overview of South America

Name _____

On the map below label a.) the twelve countries of South America, b.) its two foreign dependencies, c.) all capital cities, d.) the surrounding bodies of water.

Overview of South America

Name _____

1. South America is the _____ th largest continent in area.

2. There are many different kinds of landscapes and climates found in South America. Tell where each of the following landscapes/climates can be found in South America.

   World's largest tropical rainforest _____

   Rolling grasslands _____   _____

   One of the driest places in the world _____

   Snow-capped mountains and active volcanos _____

3. Describe each of these main land regions found in South America.

   Andes Mountains _____

   _____

   _____

   The Central Plains _____

   _____

   _____

   The Eastern Highlands _____

   _____

   _____

4. Describe each of the five major river systems found in South America.

   The Amazon River _____

   _____

   The Río de la Plata _____

   _____

   The Magdalena and Cauca Rivers _____

   _____

   The Orinoco River _____

   _____

   The São Francisco River _____

   _____

Overview of South America

(Cont.)

Name _____

5. South America has many waterfalls and lakes. Give the location of each of the following and tell one fact about each.

Angel Falls _____

_____

Cuquenán Falls _____

_____

Iguacu Falls _____

_____

Lake Maracaibo _____

_____

Lake Titicaca _____

_____

6. Although South America has a long coastline, it has few natural harbors or bays.

The best natural harbor is found at _____ .

7. List four groups of islands that are part of South America.

_____

_____

_____

_____

8. South America's hottest weather conditions are found in Argentina's _____ .

The temperature reaches _____°F there.

9. Name the South American countries through which the equator passes.

_____   _____   _____

10. Name the highest and lowest places in South America. Give their locations and altitudes.

Highest _____

_____

Lowest _____

_____

Overview of South America

Name _____

11. Most South American countries have not fully developed the large amounts of natural resources found within their boundaries and therefore have a low standard of living. Name the four countries that have the most developed economies.

    _____   _____

    _____   _____

12. Describe the differences between small and large farms in South America.

    _____

    _____

    _____

    _____

13. List seven valuable export crops that are grown in South America.

    _____   _____   _____   _____

    _____   _____   _____

14. Some farmers grow _____ or _____ for the international trade in illegal drugs. Authorities think that in Bolivia, Colombia, and Peru

    the value of these drug exports is _____ than the value of all other

                                         (higher, lower)
    export crops.

15. Approximately one-fourth of the world's coffee is grown in the South American country of

    _____ . _____ is another South
    American country that is a very large coffee producer.

16. Brazil is South America's leading manufacturing country. Name five products that are produced in this country.

    _____   _____   _____

    _____   _____

17. Tell what kind of mining is found in each of the countries listed below.

    Venezuela _____

    Bolivia _____

    Chile _____

    Peru _____

    Columbia _____

    Ecuador _____

Overview of South America

(Cont.)

18. Name the softwood whose timber is Brazil's chief forest product.

    _____

    Tell how it is used._____

    _____

    _____

19. List other products Brazil's forests yield.

    _____

    _____

20. Describe the fishing industry of Chile and Peru including the work of the fishing fleets and how their catch is used.

    _____

    _____

    _____

    _____

    _____

21. On what continents are South America's leading trade partners located?

    _____

22. Do ships or do trains play a large role in South America's transportation of goods?

    _____

23. Explain what kinds of transportation the people in poor, rural areas of South America use.

    _____

    _____

    _____

24. Radio and television are especially valued as sources of information because many of the

    people cannot _____ or _____.

25. The Galapagos Islands belong to Ecuador and are known for being the home of giant

    _____ that weigh more than 500 pounds.

Overview of South America

Name _____

26. Describe the following animals and plants that can be found in South America.

capybara _____

pirarucú _____

tapir _____

piranha _____

vicuaña and guanaco _____

anaconda _____

cacao tree _____

sisal plant _____

coca shrub _____

cinchona tree _____

quebracho tree _____

27. Define the phrase "domesticated animal." Name two animals that are believed to have been domesticated in South America and tell why they are important to the people of South America. Draw and label a picture of each animal in one of the boxes below.

A domesticated animal is _____

1. _____

2. _____

South American Land Regions

Name _____

Color the area on the map that shows the location of each of the following kinds of land regions: Andes Mountains - brown; Eastern Highlands - green; Central Plains - yellow.

Physical Features

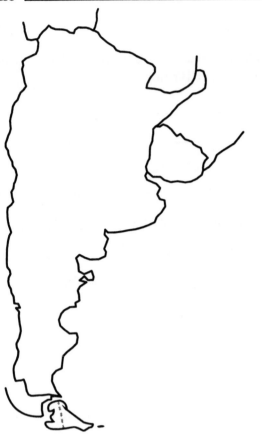

1. On the map, draw a star to mark the location of the capital of Argentina. Write the name nearby.

2. On the map, label the five countries and the body of water that border Argentina.

3. Use the symbol ∧∧∧ to show the location of the Andes Mountains in Argentina on the map.

4. There are four major land regions in Argentina. Some contain subregions. Write a brief description of each.

Northern Argentina:_____

_____

_____

    The Gran Chaco _____

_____

    Mesopotamia _____

_____

Pampa: _____

_____

The Andine: _____

_____

    Andes Mountain _____

_____

    The Piedmont _____

_____

Patagonia: _____

_____

Name _____

Physical Features (Cont.)

5. Describe the natural phenomena that occurs near the junction of the Iguaça and Paraná Rivers.

_____

_____

_____

6. The island located on the southern tip of South America that belongs to both Chile and Argentina is called _____. This island is separated from the mainland of South America by the _____.

7. The highest point in Argentina is _____. It is _____ feet above sea level. The lowest point in Argentina is _____. It is _____ feet below sea level.

8. Name the months in which Argentina's winter and summer take place.

_____

9. Describe how winds from the oceans affect Argentina's climate.

_____

_____

_____

10. Name the land features which attract recreation-seekers to Argentina. Then, in the box below, draw a picture of one of the activities you would like to do.

_____

_____

Name _____

Culture and People

1. Explain the meaning of the sun and cap on the coat of arms of Argentina.

   _____

   _____

   _____

2. People of _____ ancestry make up about 85 percent of Argentina's people.

3. Mestizos are people of mixed

   _____ and _____

   ancestry. Mestizos make up about 15 percent of Argentina's population.

4. The official language of Argentina is _____ .

5. Name the metropolitan area in which about 11 million Argentines live. _____

6. About 88 percent of Argentina's people reside in _____ or

   _____ .

7. Much of the Pampa and Patagonia is covered with ranches called _____ .

8. The national drink of the people of Argentina is a tea called _____, which is a blend of dried leaves from the native _____ tree.

9. The main religion practiced in Argentina is _____ .

10. Explain why the original Indian population of Argentina declined. _____

    _____

    _____

11. Most Argentines make what kind of meat the main part of many meals?

    _____

12. Argentina's most loved sport is _____ . Another popular sport is *pato*. In

    this game, riders on _____ try to throw a six-handled _____

    into a _____ .

13. _____ is the biggest university in South America.

Name _____

History

1. Color the flag of Argentina with its correct colors. Write the meaning of the colors and symbols found on the flag on the lines below.

   _____

   _____

   _____

   _____

   _____

   _____

2. The first European settlers to arrive in Argentina in the early 1500s were the

   _____ , who ruled for 300 years.

3. Explain how the establishment of a Portuguese trading post in 1680 influenced the growth of the Spanish colony in Argentina.

   _____

   _____

   _____

4. Identify the Sáenz Peña Law. _____

   _____

5. Identify the following dates important to Argentina's history.

   1853: _____

   _____

   1860: _____

   _____

   1930: _____

   _____

   1946: _____

   _____

Name _____

Who's Who in Argentina

Many outstanding people have made significant contributions to Argentina's growth and development. Identify each of the following influential people.

José de San Martín _____

_____

_____

Juan Perón _____

_____

_____

Carlos Saúl Menem _____

_____

_____

Alberto Ginastera _____

_____

_____

Alicia Peñalba _____

_____

_____

Prilidiano Pueyrredón _____

_____

_____

José Hernández _____

_____

_____

Domingo Faustino Sarmiento _____

_____

_____

Name _____

Map Activity

Make a pictorial map of Argentina. Draw and color a variety of pictures on the map that relate to the country of Argentina. These pictures might include animals, plants, crops, places of interest, famous people, etc. Include at least twelve different pictures. Include a key on the bottom of your map that explains what your pictures represent.

Key

Name _____

Cities to Know About

Choose two of the following cities and write three questions that you might ask others relating to that city.

Buenos Aires   Córdoba   Mar del Plata
Paraná   Rosario   Santa Fe
Tucumán

City:_____

1. Question: _____

   Answer: _____

   Source(s): _____ Page(s):_____

2. Question: _____

   Answer: _____

   Source(s): _____ Page(s):_____

3. Question: _____

   Answer: _____

   Source(s): _____ Page(s):_____

City: _____

1. Question: _____

   Answer: _____

   Source(s): _____ Page(s):_____

2. Question: _____

   Answer: _____

   Source(s): _____ Page(s):_____

3. Question: _____

   Answer: _____

   Source(s): _____ Page(s):_____

Name _____

A Proud Heritage

Read about Argentina's gauchos. Write a brief paragraph describing who they are, where they live, and what they do. Then draw a picture of a gaucho and label the different parts of his unique clothing.

_____

_____

_____

_____

_____

_____

_____

Name _____

Spanish Words to Know

Spanish is the official language in Argentina, though many Argentines also speak a second European language.

Match the Spanish word with the correct definition. Not all definitions will be used.

_____ *mestizos*

_____ *porteños*

_____ *estancias*

_____ *poncho*

_____ *pato*

_____ *asado con cuero*

_____ *pucheros*

_____ *bola*

A. a kind of stew

B. a horseback game in which two teams of riders try to grab a six-handled ball, carry it downfield, and toss it into a basket

C. cowboy

D. people of mixed Indian and European ancestry

E. a cord-and-weight sling thrown to entangle the legs of the animal being hunted

F. a barbecue at which beef is roasted in its hide over an open fire

G. people of the port

H. a blanket with a slit in the middle for the head

I. pastries stuffed with meat or fish, eggs, fruits, and vegetables

J. large ranches

Write three other Spanish words and a definition for each.

1. _____

2. _____

3. _____

Write a paragraph in English, but incorporate the three Spanish words from above.

_____
_____
_____
_____

Name _____

Physical Features

1. On the map, draw stars to mark the locations of the two capitals of Bolivia. Write the names nearby.

2. On the map, label the countries that border Bolivia.

3. Lake _____ is located on the border of Bolivia and Peru. Color this lake blue on the map. This is the world's highest navigable lake.

   Navigable means _____ .

4. Use ˄˄˄ to show the location of the Andes Mountains on the map.

5. Bolivia has four major land regions. Write about one distinctive feature of each region.

   The Andean Highlands _____

   The Yungas _____

   The Valles _____

   The Oriente _____

6. Bolivia lies _____ of the equator. Bolivian seasons are
   _(north, south)

   _____ the seasons in the northern hemisphere.
   (the same as, the opposite of)

7. The rainy season in most of Bolivia begins in _____ and ends in

   _____ .

Name _____

History

1. Color the state flag of Bolivia with its correct colors.

2. Bolivia's state flag is used only by the government. What is the difference between the "state" flag and the national flag used by the Bolivian

people?_____

_____

_____

_____

3. American Indians have lived in Bolivia

for _____ of years.
   <u>(hundreds, thousands)</u>

4. The _____ Indians had a major civilization by Lake Titicaca around A.D. 100. By the late 1300s, the _____ Indians had taken over the region. These Indians were very war-like. In the 1400s, the _____ Indians of Peru took over the region.

5. In the 1530s, Spain conquered Bolivia and made it a Spanish colony which they called

_____ or _____ .

6. The Spanish discovered the precious metal _____ in Bolivia. This became an important source of wealth for Spain.

7. In the 1800s, the country of _____ helped Bolivia win its independence from Spain.

8. Bolivia is named for _____, who helped lead the country to independence.

9. How did Bolivia lose over half of its total land area?_____

_____

_____

10. Why did Bolivian workers strike often in the 1980s? _____

_____

_____

Name _____

Lost Land

On August 6, 1825, Bolivia became an independent republic. When Bolivia gained its independence, it claimed much more land than it does today. During the War of the Pacific (1879–1883), Bolivia lost its land along the Pacific coast to Chile, giving up this land's rich nitrate deposits and its access to the ocean shipping port. Powerful Brazil annexed three sections of Bolivia. Peru gained a small section of Bolivia. In 1932, war broke out between Bolivia and Paraguay over a piece of land. Bolivia lost and signed the land over to Paraguay in 1938.

On the map below, the land Bolivia once claimed is marked with slanted lines. Look at a current political map of Bolivia and the surrounding countries. Then color the land Bolivia lost to Peru with yellow, to Brazil with blue, to Paraguay with red, and to Chile with green. Be sure to add these colors to the key.

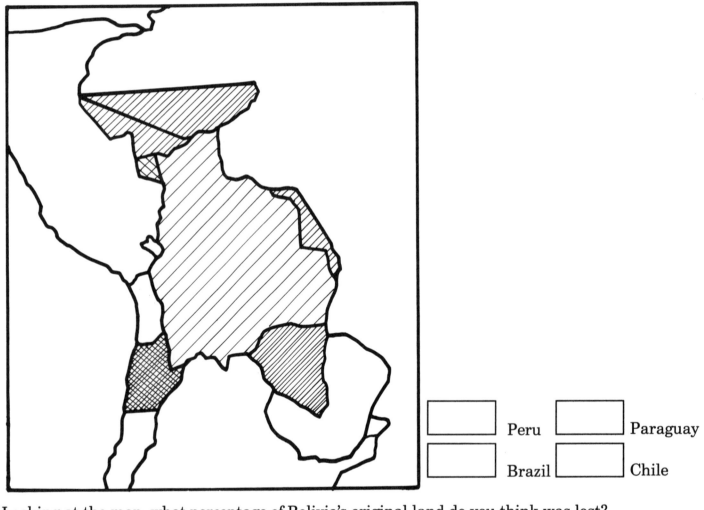

☐ Peru   ☐ Paraguay
☐ Brazil ☐ Chile

Looking at the map, what percentage of Bolivia's original land do you think was lost?

_____ 10%   _____ 25%   _____ 50%   _____ 80%

What do you think was Bolivia's most devastating loss of land and why? Answer this question on another paper. Be sure to use complete sentences.

Name _____

Cities of Bolivia

La Paz

   La Paz is the actual capital of Bolivia. It has the executive and legislative branches of government and is Bolivia's largest city and commercial center. The city is located on the slopes and bottom of a canyon in the *altiplano* (high plateau) region. Peaks of the Andes Mountains tower over the city. About one million people live in La Paz. Adobe and brick homes crouch on the hillsides and skyscrapers rise from the valley depths. A modern residential area is located on the floor of the canyon. Aymaran Indians make up about half of the La Paz population. The city has an open market where people can purchase vegetables, fruit, whole pigs, household goods, and hot, fresh coffee. At 12,000 feet (3660 meters) above sea level, La Paz is the highest capital in the world.

Cochabamba

   This city rests in the highly populated, fertile Cochabamba Basin. Its climate is more mild than that of the antiplano region. It sits in a valley at 8,376 feet (2553 meters) above sea level. It has a population of about 317,000. A comfortable climate and attractive setting have helped make Cochabamba the third largest city in Bolivia. A big plaza in the city's center honors the date when local patriots began to fight against Spanish rule in the War of Independence. Travel from Cochabamba to La Paz is possible by air, rail, and highway.

Write the name of the city which most closely fits the phrase.

_____ about 1,000,000 people live here

_____ located in a basin

_____ located in the altiplano region

_____ plaza honoring War of Independence

_____ mild, comfortable climate

_____ highest capital in the world

_____ skyscrapers in valley

_____ About 317,000 people live here

_____ modern residential area on canyon floor

Read about Sucre, the official capital of Bolivia. Write a paragraph comparing Sucre to La Paz. Your comparison should include at least one way that these cities are similar and one way that they are different.

Name _____

V.I.B. (Very Important Bolivian)

Simón Bolívar was so important to Bolivia that the country is named for him. Bolívar was vital to several South American countries in gaining their independence. Research Simón Bolívar. Below, write about what *you think* of Bolívar and his life. Give specific examples from his life that support what you think. For example, if you admire Bolívar, state that. Then, give specific instances from his life that support your belief that he is an admirable person.

_____

_____

_____

_____

_____

_____

_____

_____

_____

_____

_____

_____

_____

_____

_____

_____

Name _____

Women's Clothing

Many working-class Bolivians, called *cholos*, wear the clothing of their ancestors. The traditional dress includes a brightly colored skirt with many underskirts, known as a *polleras*. These women also frequently wear a woolen shawl over a blouse. Red is a favorite clothing color. Hair is often worn in two long braids.

A person can learn a lot about a Bolivian woman by the hat she wears. Here are some examples: The Aymará women of La Paz wear black bowler hats. The Campesina women of the Cochabamba valleys wear tall, white hats with black ribbons. The number and form of the loops of ribbons around the crown tell if the wearer is single, married, or a widow. Quechua women of the highlands east of the Altiplano wear flat-topped hats made of white wool. These hats are taller and broader than the Aymará bowler hats.

On the lines provided, name the women who wear each hat and where they live. Then draw a line from each hat to the place on the map where it is worn.

women: _____

location: _____

women: _____

location: _____

women: _____

location: _____

Name _____

Mamoré River Trip

Locate the cities Guajará-Mirim and Trinidad on a map. Locate the Mamoré River on a map. Then, read the following page from a diary which describes a boat trip down this river from Guajará-Mirim to Trinidad.

Dear Diary,

   I am traveling on a cattle boat down the Mamoré River in Bolivia. The boat is a double-decker wooden barge with an old, smoky gasoline engine. The cattle are kept on the lower level, and the passengers ride on the bridge, or upper level. I sleep in a hammock. The sun is hot and intense and the cattle smell bad, but the scenery is beautiful. We travel through thick jungles filled with fantastic birds. I see green and yellow macaws, white egrets and storks. Blue kingfishers swoop into the water and emerge with fish in their beaks. The water is a dirty brown so I am unable to see fish, but I spy the pink dolphin which lives in the Amazon River and many of its tributaries. South American alligators, known as caimans, sunbathe on sandbars we pass. It is the end of the rainy season, so the river is swollen and driftwood and other debris float on the water.

As we pass the villages, the native men paddle their canoes out to our boat to try to sell food and wild animal skins, usually alligator and jaguar. The trip will take six days, but already I feel myself slipping into the rhythm of the river.

Define the following terms:

barge _____

hammock _____

tributaries _____

debris _____

jaguar _____

Would you like to take a trip like this? Why or why not?

_____

_____

_____

_____

On another paper, create a picture which shows what you think the river and the surrounding landscape looks like. Be sure to include the animals. Look up unfamiliar animals in a reference book so you can include them in your picture.

Name _____

Balsa Boats

The people who live in Bolivia on Lake Titicaca, the highest lake in the world, make boats out of dried reeds. The boats are known as balsa boats. The reeds are harvested and laid in the sun to dry. After drying, they are made into tight bundles which form the base and side of the boat. Sometimes a boat has a sail also made from reeds. Boats are removed from the lake when they are not being used. This allows the reeds to dry out between trips and prevents rot.

• **Are reeds or grass really good boat building material?**

What do you think? Make a guess or hypothesis before you do the following experiment. Then keep notes on the experiment using the chart on page 26.

Materials: Students or teacher gather different grasses and dry them. Grasses should come from wet areas and have different circumferences. Grasses should be harvested whole. A chart should be made listing the different types of grasses, including a sample of each type of grass. This chart will allow students to compare their pieces of grass stem to the actual plant on the chart. You also need wood (sticks or bark). Include whole wood samples on your chart. Margarine tubs, medium-sized rubber bands, and water complete the materials list.

#1 Comparing Grasses: Take a small sample of each of the grasses, approximately 1" in length. Samples may be marked with a permanent marker so students know what sample they have. This can be correlated with same grass types on the chart. Place all samples of grass in a margarine tub (or tubs) filled with water. Each day, record the status of the grasses. Have any sunk? Do they all float? Does the size of the grass stem seem to matter? This experiment should run at least one week, but may be conducted as long as you wish.

#2 Comparing Grass with wood: Wood is also used as a boat-building material. In this experiment, students will compare the floating capabilities of wood versus grass. Conduct this experiment the same way you did #1, but this time add the different types of wood that were collected. Woods that are difficult to distinguish should also be marked with a permanent marker. Which floats longest, grass or wood? The experiment should be conducted until boat materials become saturated and begin to sink.

#3 Weight Experiments/Comparing Grasses: Cut 10 three-inch lengths of each of the grass samples. Make bundles of 10 of each of the like grasses and tie them together with rubber bands. Make sure the rubber band is at the midpoint of the bundle. Rubber bands do not float. Test this yourself. To see how much weight the different grasses can hold, continue to add rubber bands, tightly wrapped, to each bundle. How many rubber bands does it take to sink each bundle? Which bundle held the most weight? Why do you think you got the results you did?

Name _____

Balsa Boats Experiment Results

Use for #1 and #2.

Grass or Wood (number or name these)	Observations (How many days does it take for each to sink?)

Use for #3.

Grasses or Wood	Observations (Number of rubber bands it takes to sink.)

Name _____

Map Activity

Make a pictorial map of Bolivia. Draw and color a variety of pictures on the map that relate to the country of Bolivia. These pictures might include animals, plants, crops, places of interest, famous people, etc. Include at least 12 different topics. Include a key on the bottom of your map that explains what your pictures represent.

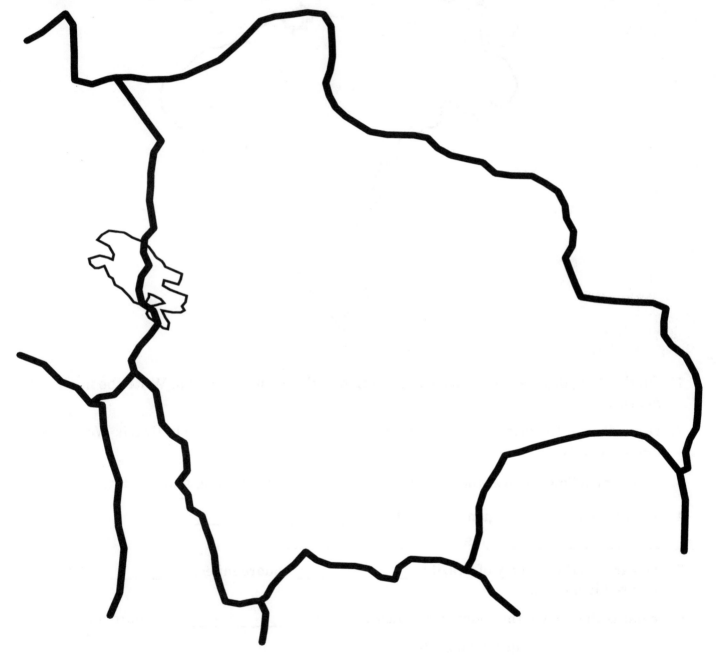

Key

Name _____

Physical Features

1. On the map, draw a star to mark the location of the capital of Brazil. Write the name nearby.

2. Draw dots on the map to mark the location of the two largest cities in Brazil. Write the names nearby.

3. Label the following rivers on the map: Amazon, Madeira, Paraná, and São Francisco Rivers.

4. The three main land regions of Brazil are _____,
   _____ , and _____ .

5. The area of the country of Brazil is _____ square miles, or _____ square kilometers.

6. What is the area of the country in which you live? _____ square miles, or
   _____ square kilometers

   How much larger or smaller is your country than Brazil? _____ square miles,
   or _____ square kilometers

History

Name _____

1. Color the Brazilian flag using the correct colors. On the lines below, describe the meaning of each color and write the motto found on the flag.

_____

_____

_____

_____

_____

_____

_____

2. Brazil was named after _____ .

3. Brazil has _____ states and _____ federal district.

   This federal district encompassses _____ .

4. The major Indian groups that lived in Brazil before the Europeans arrived were the

   _____ and _____ .

5. One of the emperors of Brazil, Pedro II, took office at the early age of _____ .
   He helped Brazil progress in many ways. List them below.

   _____

   _____

   _____

   _____

   _____

   _____

6. Brazil became a republic on _____ .

Name _____

Culture and People

1. Brazil has _____ miles or

   _____ kilometers of
   coastline. Thousands of people go to the
   beach to enjoy various kinds of recreation

   such as _____ .

2. Brazil's number one sport is

   _____ . Other

   popular sports are _____

   _____ .

3. _____ is
   Brazil's most famous festival. It is
   celebrated during the four days preceding
   Lent.

4. Three main ethnic groups make up

   Brazil's population: _____ , _____ , and people of

   _____ ancestry. The mixed groups include *caboclos*, who are

   _____ and *mulattoes*, who are

   _____ .

5. _____ is the nation's official language, though Indian

   groups in the Amazon area still speak traditional languages.

6. Government buildings in Brazil are known for their modern architecture. Study some of the
   government buildings and draw and label one of them in the box below.

Name _____

Cities in Brazil

Belém   Manaus   Rio de Janeiro   Santos
Belo Horizonte   Pôrto Alegre   Salvador   São Paulo
Brasília   Recife

Find the location of each of the cities listed above on a map of Brazil.

Choose one of the above cities in Brazil to study. Write a description of this city to share with others.

Name of the city:

_____

I chose this city to study because _____

_____ .

The population of this city was _____ in the year _____ .

Write a description of the city.

_____

_____

_____

_____

_____

_____

_____

_____

_____

_____

_____

_____

_____

Name _____

Chief Products of Brazil

List the name of a Brazilian product in each category and draw a small picture of it in the space provided. Conduct research in an encyclopedia or dictionary about how that product is produced. Write a description in the space provided.

Product	Production Procedures
Agriculture:	
Mining:	
Manufacturing and Processing:	
Forest Products:	

Name _____

Animals of the Rainforest

The Amazon Region occupies most of northern Brazil. It is mostly covered by jungle and tropical rainforest called *selva*. Read and discover what animals live in this region. Below, draw and label at least eight different animals in their rainforest habitat.

Name _____

Portuguese Language

The official language of Brazil is Portuguese. Find a Portuguese dictionary, an encyclopedia that includes the Portuguese language, or a book on Portuguese. Use the book(s) to help you complete the activities below.

1. Write the correct numbers above the Portuguese words for them.

   _____ _____ _____ _____

   três   oito   quatro   um or uma

   _____ _____ _____ _____

   dez   sete   seis   nove

2. In Portuguese, write the words for the numbers in the correct order. Put a comma between the words to show where each word ends. Write the name of the reference book, including the page number, where you found the information.

   _____

   _____

   Source: _____ Page(s): _____

3. Draw at least three objects in the box below and label them in English and in Portuguese. You may use the back of this paper if you want to draw and label more objects. It is important that you check to see that you have spelled the words correctly. Learn to say some of the words.

   Source: _____ Page(s) _____

   _____
   | |
   | |
   | |
   | |
   | |
   | |
   | |
   | |
   | |
   | |
   |_____|

Name _____

Map Activity

Make a pictorial map of Brazil. Draw and color a variety of pictures on the map that relate to the country of Brazil. These pictures might include animals, plants, crops, places of interest, famous people, etc. Include at least 12 different topics. Include a key on the bottom of your map that explains what your pictures represent.

Key

Name _____

Physical Features

1. On the map, draw a star to mark the location of the capital of Chile. Write the name nearby.

2. On the map, label the three countries and the body of water that border Chile.

3. What are the names of the major islands that belong to Chile?

   _____

   _____

   _____

4. Give a brief description of the three land regions of Chile.

   The Northern Desert _____

   _____

   _____

   _____

   The Central Valley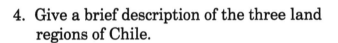

   _____

   _____

   The Archipelago

   _____

   _____

5. Tell about some of the attractions of the Lake Country area, just south of the Bío-Bío River, which is a popular summer vacation spot.

   _____

   _____

Name _____

Culture and People

1. The Chilean coat of arms bears the Spanish words "Por la Razon o la Fuerza" which means . .

   _____

   _____

   Color the coat of arms.

2. Most Chileans are a mix of

   _____ and

   _____ ancestry.

   These Chileans follow the

   _____

   religion and speak _____ .

3. Name three groups of Indians found in Chile.

   _____

   _____

   _____

4. Describe the different kinds of housing found in Chilean cities.

   _____

   _____

   _____

5. Explain why many poor, rural Chileans moved to the cities since the 1940s and the result.

   _____

   _____

   _____

6. Name the occupation of most rural Chileans. _____

   Some work on large farms, owned by the wealthy, as _____ or

   _____ .

7. Chile's most popular spectator sport is _____ .

Name _____

History

1. Color the flag of Chile in its correct colors. Give the meaning of the colors/symbols found on the flag.

   _____

   _____

   _____

   _____

   _____

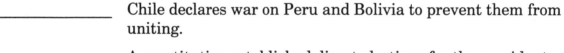

2. Fill in the dates of the following historic events that took place in Chile:

   _____ Conquered by the Incas.

   _____ Spaniards invade and conquer Chile.

   _____ Chile gains its independence from Spain.

   _____ Chile declares war on Peru and Bolivia to prevent them from uniting.

   _____ A constitution established direct elections for the president and the separation of church and state.

   _____ Salvador Allende Gossens, a Marxist, elected president.

   _____ Democratic type of government established.

3. Explain why the Spaniards began to explore Chile and what they did when they could not find what they were searching for.

   _____

   _____

   _____

4. The first European explorer to reach Chile was _____ .

5. The founder of Santiago was _____ .

6. The Irishman who defeated the Spanish in 1817 was _____ .

7. The 1989 president-elect of Chile was _____ .

Name _____

Map Activity

Draw and color a variety of pictures around the map that relate to the country of Chile. These pictures might include animals, plants, crops, places of interest, famous people, etc. Include at least 12 different topics. Include a key on the bottom of your map that explains what your pictures represent.

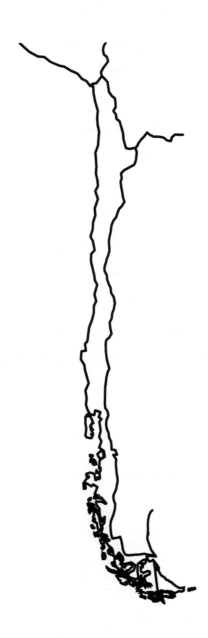

Key

Name _____

Cities to Know About

Choose two of the following cities. Research and write three questions that you might ask others relating to each city.

Santiago   **Concepción**   **Valparaíso**   **Viña del Mar**

City: _____

1. Question: _____

   Answer: _____

   _____

   Source: _____ Page(s): _____

2. Question: _____

   Answer: _____

   _____

   Source: _____ Page(s): _____

3. Question: _____

   Answer: _____

   _____

   Source: _____ Page(s): _____

City: _____

1. Question: _____

   Answer: _____

   _____

   Source: _____ Page(s): _____

2. Question: _____

   Answer: _____

   _____

   Source: _____ Page(s): _____

3. Question: _____

   Answer: _____

   _____

   Source: _____ Page(s): _____

Name _____

Spanish Words to Know

Match the Chilean terms with the correct definitions. Not all definitions will be used.

_____ callampas

_____ fundos

_____ huasos

_____ plaza

_____ chilli

_____ cazuela de ave

_____ pastel de choclo

A. herbal tea

B. baked corn casserole

C. mushrooms—a word that refers to the slums in Chile because they seem to pop up overnight

D. huge estates

E. hearty chicken, rice and vegetable stew

F. farm workers

G. public square

H. where the land ends; Chile's name

I. Chilean cowboy

Illustrate one of the terms above.

Research the Spanish language. Write ten Spanish words and the definition for each one.

1. _____
2. _____
3. _____
4. _____
5. _____
6. _____
7. _____
8. _____
9. _____
10. _____

Name _____

Physical Features

1. On the map, draw a star to mark the location of the capital of Colombia. Write the name nearby.

2. Label the countries and bodies of water that border Colombia.

3. Use ∧∧∧ to mark the location of the Andes Mountains on the map.

4. _____ is Colombia's highest mountain. It rises

   _____ feet, or

   _____ meters, above sea level. Use a small cross (+) to mark its location on the map.

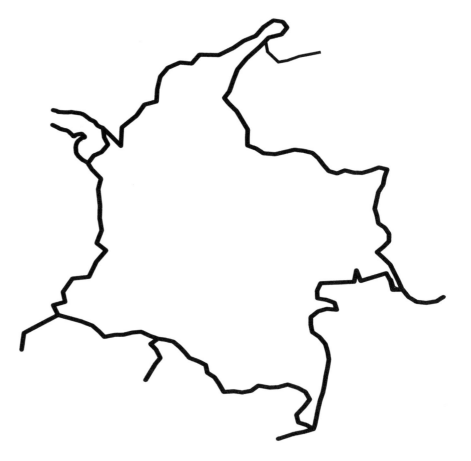

5. Describe the physical features of the three major land regions that make up Colombia.

   Coastal Lowlands _____

   _____

   _____

   Andes Mountains _____

   _____

   _____

   Eastern Plains _____

   _____

   _____

6. Define *llanos* _____

7. The Nevado del Ruiz, located in the Andes Mountains west of Bogotá, is an _____

   _____ . Use a red triangle to mark its location on the map.

Name _____

History

1. Color the flag of Colombia in its correct colors.

2. The yellow stripe in Colombia's flag

    represents _____

    _____ .

    The red stands for _____

    _____

    and the blue stands for _____

    _____ .

3. _____
    inhabited Colombia before the arrival of
    the Spanish.

4. The Chibcha were an advanced civilization

    living in the Andes Mountains. They were conquered by the

    _____ , who named the city of

    Bogotá after the Cibcha chief _____ .

5. After the Spanish invasion of Colombia, a new population of people was created by the
    intermarriage of the Spanish and Indian peoples. A person of mixed Indian and Spanish

    heritage is known as a _____ . Today, _____ to _____
    percent of Colombians are of mixed Spanish and Indian descent.

6. Colombia's movement towards independence from the Spanish began in 1780 and 1781,

    when people were angered by new _____ .

7. Spain was finally defeated by Colombia in the year _____ . The decisive battle,

    known as _____ was led by Venezuelan General _____ .

8. In 1903, Colombia lost _____ when the Colombian Senate refused
    to allow the United States to build a canal from the Atlantic to the Pacific Ocean.
    Panama revolted.

9. In 1922, Colombia was paid _____ million by the U.S. for the loss of Panama.

10. Colombia is named after explorer _____ .

Extension: On another paper, describe what happened in Colombia during the period known as
    La Violencia (The Violence).

Name _____

Puracé National Park

Puracé is a national park in Colombia. The park has a snow-covered, active volcano which is more than 15,000 feet tall. *Páramos*, which are high, bleak Andean plateaus or alpine meadows, are also found in the park. The wet, rainy meadows of the *páramos* are home to many types of animals. The park is a refuge for the pudu, the mountain tapir, the condor, and the spectacled bear. Puracé became a national park in 1961 and covers 320 square miles (830 sq. km).

Your Mission: You are a wildlife biologist and an expert on one of the three endangered animals protected by Puracé. Descriptions of the animals can be found on the following page. You have been invited to Colombia to document that these endangered species still live. Keep a 10-day diary, recording where you travel in the park and what you see. Remember, these animals are rare and very difficult to find. Your diary needs to be realistic. Since you are tracking the animal it would be natural to see signs of it before you find it. For example, you may find a spectacled bear's nest of branches and leaves, or a burrowing tunnel marking the trail of a tapir. You may see deer tracks that you can follow. Make up an adventure. Find your animals and have fun!

Name _____

Puracé National Park
Animal Descriptions

Spectacled Bear

This is the only kind of bear found in South America. Mostly black, with yellow or white patches of fur around its eyes, the spectacled bear prefers to live in cool, high forests, including the *páramo* area of Puracé National Park. This bear makes nests for itself with branches and leaves, but it rarely stays in one place for long and may travel long distances in search of food. It eats fruits, leaves, and roots. The spectacled bear is in danger of becoming extinct because its forest homes are being destroyed and because it has been overhunted. Protected areas like Puracé National Park are the only places these animals are safe from humans.

Mountain Tapir

This animal is similar to a hog or boar in appearance, though it is related to the horse and the rhinoceros. There are two kinds of South American tapirs, lowland and mountain. The mountain tapir is quite rare. Like the lowland tapir, it lives by water. Tapirs love to swim! This animal makes tunnel-like trails through the undergrowth. This makes the animal particularly difficult to see. It is found in elevations of 6,500 to 14,500 feet and lives in heavy plant undergrowth. Tapirs eat twigs and leaves off trees and shrubs, as well as any fruits or vegetables they can find. The mountain tapir has long been hunted for its meat and thick hide. Its forest habitat is quickly disappearing due to extensive logging and agricultural activity.

Pudu

These tiny deer are only about one foot high and are known for their shyness. They have tiny, spiked antlers. Pudu live in the *páramo* as well as forested areas which range from sea level to altitudes of 10,000 feet (3,000 meters). Pudu are found only in South America. These animals do not have a permanent den or nesting site. They roam in herds or alone in search of food. Deer are herbivores: they eat only plants. Their diet consists mostly of grasses, flowers, buds, leaves, and in lean times, bark or twigs. Pudu are the smallest of all deer. Their coat is rough and brown or gray. Amazingly, these deer are considered hunting trophies. Habitat destruction, though, is the biggest threat to their continued existence.

Name _____

Birds of Colombia

Read the information below. In the box draw a picture of the bird described. Be sure to pay attention to size, wingspan, markings, and color so your drawing is accurate. You may want to make a rough sketch of the bird as you read and then draw it again neatly on this page.

Sword-Billed Hummingbird

The male sword-billed hummingbird grows to about 5.8 inches tall. It is known for its enormously long bill which is heavy and slightly upturned. The bill is about 4 inches long. That is almost as long as the bird is tall! The bird has a bronze head and bronze-green feathers covering the rest of its back. Its throat is brown-black and its underparts are bright green. Its 2-inch-long split tail is bronze green. This bird lives in the Andes Mountains in Colombia, as well as in Ecuador, Peru, and Bolivia.

Blue-Crowned Motmot

Motmots are a small family of tropical birds. Motmots live in dark forests, feeding on fruits, insects, and reptiles. The blue-crowned motmot grows from 15 to 17 inches tall. It has a long bill, approximately 3 inches long. The very top of its head and forehead are black, and the sides of the head are a brilliant turquoise that changes to an ultramarine blue on the lower sides and back of the bird's head. The back is grass green with a tinge of light blue on the tips of the wings. It has a black spot bordered by turquoise blue in the middle of its olive green and cinnamon chest. The tail is longer than its body and is green, becoming blue at the very end, tipped with black. This is a vibrantly colored bird with a very, very long tail.

Extension: Write a description of an animal or bird and have a classmate try to draw the animal from what you wrote.

Name _____

Smuggling

The Problem

Animals are stolen from South America, smuggled to different parts of the world, and sold to people as pets for a tremendous profit. It is illegal to remove animals from South America without a permit. So much of the continent is densely forested that it is difficult to catch people illegally trapping the animals.

The smugglers are interested only in the profit they can make. They do not care about the laws or the animals. Smugglers have been known to put over 300 birds in one box to illegally ship them out of South America. If only half of the birds live, the smugglers believe that it has been profitable. These people will also try to make animals more attractive to buyers. They have been known to paint green parakeets fantastic colors: red, purples, oranges, and yellows. When the bird molts, the painted feathers drop out, leaving the bird its original green color once again. By this time, however, the crook is far away.

• On another paper, write a paragraph telling why you think that it should or should not be illegal to sell South American animals as pets. Then devise some ways the South American government could fight this problem and write about them.

The Solution?

South American officials are battling the problem of animal-napping and smuggling. When they discover an illegal shipment of animals, they arrest the culprits and return the animals to South America. Captured animals are sent to a center for rehabilitation with the hope that they can be released into the wild.

Even when the officials feel the animal is ready to be released into the wild, they often don't know where the animal originated. To add to this dilemma, there are many subspecies of any one species. This means that a parrot from the rain forest of Brazil is different from the same species of parrot from the forests of Colombia. It is extremely difficult, though, to determine these minute differences. If an animal is released in the wrong area, it could change the face of the population in that area, perhaps endangering the survival of the animals already living there.

• Do you think animals should be rehabilitated and released into the wild? Why or why not? On another paper, explain your views in a paragraph.

Name _____

Poetry

Colombians have great regard for writers, especially poets. Writers are so admired that many teachers, lawyers, doctors, and other professional people spend their spare time writing poetry. Colombians boast that more poets than generals have been elected president.

Below are some descriptions of Colombian life. After each, write a *couplet* that will give readers a feeling for what you read.

A *couplet* is a verse composed of two lines which can, but do not have to, rhyme. One of the keys to writing good verse is to take your time and think about the flow and sound of your words when they are read aloud. It is not unusual for poetry to require more rewriting than descriptive writing.

Colombians enjoy thick stews and soups. One of their favorites is a delicious soup made from tender chicken, potatoes, and corn. The soup is called *ajiaco* (ah hee AH koh). Potatoes are a staple in the diets of many Colombians.

Example: *Bubbling, steaming, mouth-watering smells fill my head with memories*
Of fall earth bursting with potatoes, waiting to become ajiaco.

_____

_____

Colombia is the only country in South America which borders both the Pacific Ocean and the Caribbean Sea in the Atlantic Ocean. The many rivers and swamps provided early Colombian people with a natural transportation route. Native peoples traveled, migrated, and traded with each other using dug-out canoes. Imagine traveling along a coast in the turquoise blue of the Caribbean Sea and looking towards a dark green, mysterious rain forest teeming with the sounds of life.

_____

_____

Soccer is Colombia's national sport. Two teams with 11 players on each side try to kick or hit a round white and black ball into the other team's goal using any body part except the hands. Soccer was invented in England, but has become the world's most popular sport. More than 140 countries world-wide have soccer teams. Playing this game well requires a lot of athletic skill and ability. Players need to know how to kick, pass, tackle, fake, dribble, and head the ball.

_____

_____

Name _____

Picaresque

The *picaresque* is a type of story where the main character is a villainous, nasty, unlikable person. This type of story is not written with one continuous plot, but is written as a series of events or incidents that describe the main character's life. These bits and pieces of life are then put together to create an entire story. The *picaresque* was invented in Spain, but Colombians are famous for this type of writing.

Choose one of the following subjects. Research your choice, thinking carefully about the types of people who would have been involved. Using what you've learned, create a main character who is a "bad guy." Write about one event that happened during the life of your main character.

slavery   Spanish invasion   La Violencia

piracy   conquistadors   bull fighting

_____

_____

_____

_____

_____

_____

_____

_____

_____

_____

_____

_____

_____

_____

Extension: As a class, create a "bad guy." Then, write a class *picaresque* featuring your "bad guy" as the main character. Each day, the story is given to a different student who reads what has been written so far and adds one written event in the main character's life to that. When everyone has had a turn to add to the class book, the *picaresque* is complete.

Name _____

El Dorado

The Chibchas people lived in Colombia long before the Spanish invaded. They believed that a meteor fell to earth creating a huge hole that became Guatavita Lake. This lake was special to the Chibchas, so they held ceremonies at its shore, including initiation ceremonies for new Chibchas leaders. A new chief would cover his body in a sticky, glue-like substance. Then gold dust would be sprinkled all over the glue, making the chief into a living golden statue. The golden leader was rowed on a raft to the middle of the lake where he would dive in. The gold would wash off in the water. This was the new chief's way of offering gold to the lake. At the same time, people in the raft and on shore would throw gold and jewels into the lake as a further offering.

This Chibchas ceremony was probably the basis for the fanatical search for El Dorado, the fictitious kingdom of fabulous riches and wealth. The Spanish pursued this dream with a vengeance. The legend of El Dorado was the cause of much death and strife for the native people of Colombia.

1. Create a Colombian treasure map. This map may include only a portion of the country or may cover all of Colombia. Draw natural features and cities as landmarks on the map.

2. Write a letter that goes with the map, giving hints and clues to where a treasure hunter should start as well as warnings against dangers. Use directions, landmarks, or facts to direct treasure hunters on your map.

3. Trade your map and treasure hunt description with another student. Each of you should try to locate El Dorado.

Note: There are no rules. Make the maps and descriptions fair, but fun. There should be a final location for El Dorado, but you may make the hunt as mysterious and difficult as you would like. For instance, you might use a riddle, or a treasure hunter might have to collect clues from each landmark on the map to discover where El Dorado is. Use your imagination. Happy hunting!

Name _____

Map Activity

Make a pictorial map of Colombia. Draw and color a variety of pictures on the map that relate to the country of Colombia. These pictures might include animals, plants, crops, places of interest, famous people, etc. Include at least 12 different topics. Include a key on the bottom of your map that explains what your pictures represent.

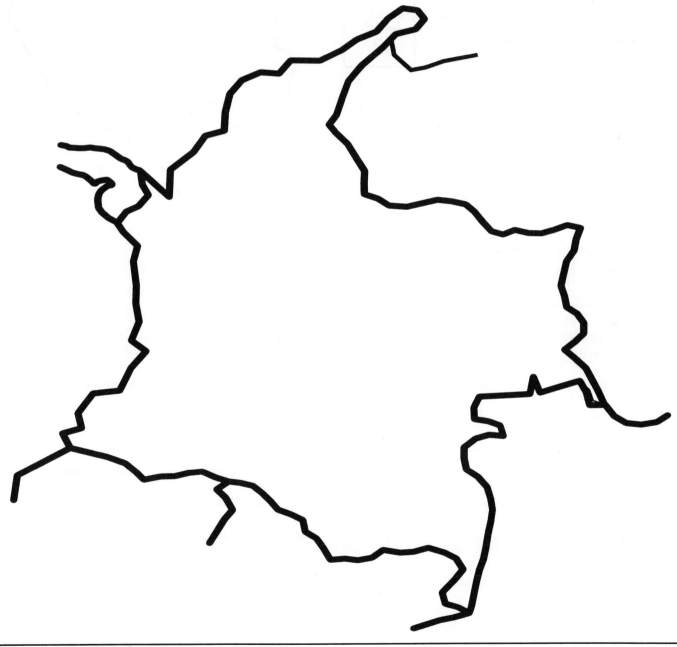

Key

Name _____

Physical Features

1. On the map, draw a star to mark the location of the capital of Ecuador. Write the name nearby.

2. Write the names of the two countries and body of water that border Ecuador on the map.

3. Draw the equator on the map.

4. Locate the Andes Mountains. Label them on the map using the symbol ∧∧∧ .

5. Ecuador was named for

_____

_____ .

Ecuador is the Spanish word

for _____ .

Galapagos Islands

6. On the map, draw a dot to mark the location of Ecuador's largest city. Write the name nearby.

7. The Galapagos Islands, approximately 600 miles (970 kilometers) off the coast, belong to Ecuador. These islands are known for their unusual _____ and

_____ .

8. Ecuador is one of the _____ countries of South America.
   (smallest, largest)

9. The country contains large _____ deposits.

10. The _____ and _____ of the Andes Mountains are where about half of the people of Ecuador live.

11. A big _____ is located east of the Andes Mountains. Not many people live there.

12. Ecuador has three land regions. Write a brief description of each.

    The Coastal Lowland _____

    The Andes Highland _____

    The Eastern Lowland _____

Name _____

History

1. Color Ecuador's flag with its correct colors.

2. Communication in Ecuador is very primitive. Write two facts that support this statement.

   _____

   _____

   _____

   _____

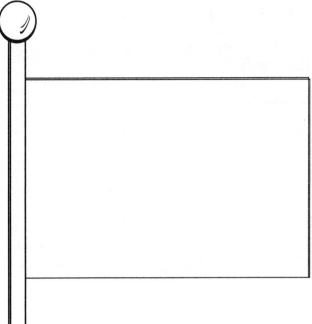

3. Write a fact that you think is important about each of the following periods in Ecuador's history.

   Indian Period: _____

   _____

   _____

   Spanish Rule: _____

   _____

   Independence: _____

   _____

   During the 1900s: _____

   _____

In the box below, illustrate one of the facts you just listed.

Name _____

Culture and People

1. What do people do at the market shown in the picture?

   _____

   _____

   _____

   _____

   _____

   _____

2. Most Ecuadorians speak what language?

   _____

3. Why are some children unable to attend school in the rural areas of Ecuador?

   _____

   _____

4. Many Ecuadorians cannot read or write. How do you think this affects their lives?

   _____

   _____

   _____

5. About 10 percent of Ecuador's population, mostly people of European ancestry, make up the

   _____ group in the country.
   (wealthiest, poorest)

6. Indians and *mestizos,* who are people of mixed _____ and

   _____ ancestry, each make up about 40 percent of Ecuador's population.

7. _____ , whose ancestors were slaves, form 10 percent of the population.

8. Describe what it is like to live in an Indian Village in Ecuador.

   _____

   _____

   _____

   _____

   _____

Name _____

Cities in Ecuador

Ambato	Esmeraldas	Machala	Portoviejo
Cuenca	Guayaquil	Manta	Quito

Find the location of each of these cities on a map of Ecuador.

Choose one of the above cities in Ecuador to study. Write a description of this city to share with others.

Name of city: _____

I chose this city to study because _____

_____

The population of this city was _____ in the year _____ .

Write a description of the city.

_____

_____

_____

_____

_____

_____

_____

_____

_____

_____

_____

_____

_____

_____

_____

_____

Name _____

Galapagos Islands

1. The Galapagos Islands were once known as the

   _____

   _____ .

2. The Galapagos Islands are owned

   by _____ .

3. Name the five largest Galapagos Islands.

   _____

   _____

   _____

   _____

   _____

   Label these five islands on the map.

4. Label the ocean which surrounds the islands on the map.

5. The Galapagos Islands span about _____ square miles (_____ square kilometers).

6. Most of the islands are _____ peaks.

7. The islands are also called the _____ de _____ .

8. Research the Galapagos Islands. Record here some facts you find interesting about these islands.

   _____

   _____

   _____

   _____

   _____

   _____

   Source: _____ Page(s): _____

Name _____

Galapagos Islands Art

Read as much as possible about the Galapagos Islands, which are owned by Ecuador. Draw, color, and label pictures relating to these islands in the frame below. Cut out the frame and display the picture in your classroom.

G
A
L
A
P
A
G
O
S

I
S
L
A
N
D
S

Name _____

Map Activity

Make a pictorial map of Ecuador. Draw and color a variety of pictures on the map that relate to the country of Ecuador. These pictures might include animals, plants, crops, places of interest, famous people, etc. Include at least 12 different topics. Include a key on the bottom of your map that explains what your pictures represent.

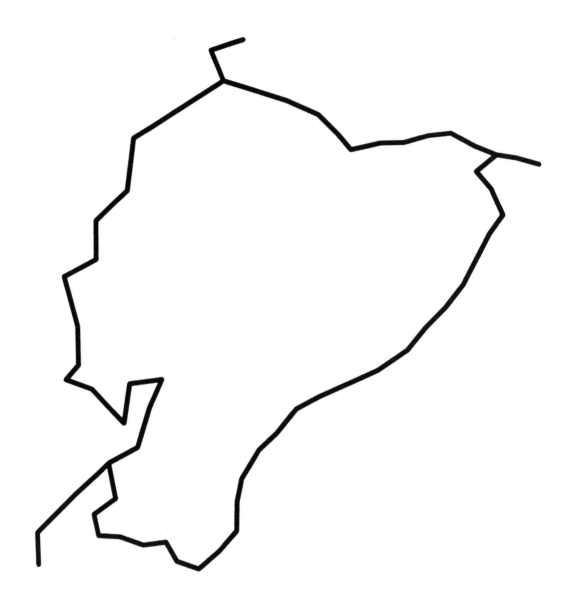

Key

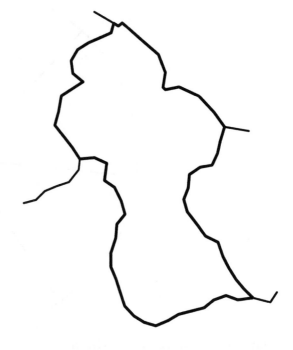

Name _____

Physical Features

1. On the map, draw a star to mark the location of the capital of Guyana. Write the name nearby.

2. On the map, label the three countries and the body of water that border Guyana.

3. Give a description of each of the three main land regions found in Guyana.

   The coastal plain _____

   _____

   _____

   The inland forest _____

   _____

   _____

   The highland _____

   _____

4. The four main rivers of Guyana flow north into the Atlantic Ocean. Name these rivers.

   _____   _____

   _____   _____

5. There are many spectacular waterfalls located throughout Guyana. Tell where each of the following waterfalls is located and give the height or drop distance for each one.

   King George VI Falls _____

   Great Falls _____

   Kaieteur Falls _____

General Information

Name _____

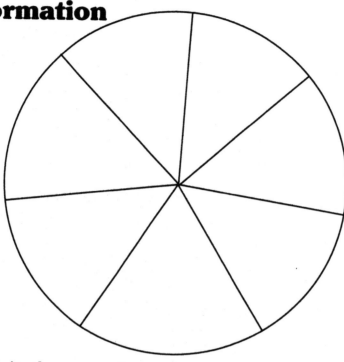

1. In the circle above, write the names of seven important crops grown in Guyana.

2. The two largest ethnic groups found in Guyana are the _____ and the _____.

3. The official language of the people of Guyana is _____, but many of the people speak a broken form of English called _____.

4. Guyana's East Indians speak _____ and _____ .

5. The East Indians of Guyana live in rural areas and work on _____ or on small farms where they grow _____ and _____. Their ancestors came from _____. Some East Indians have moved to cities and towns and work as _____ , _____ , and _____ .

6. The blacks of Guyana live in the cities and towns and many work as skilled workers in the _____ mills and _____ mines. Others are _____ , _____ , and _____ .

7. The most important kind of tree that grows in Guyana is the _____ , because it is used for making _____ , where boats can dock to load and unload cargo.

8. Some Amerindians live in remote forest areas. Some make their living by _____ and others by _____ or _____ .

Name _____

History

1. Color the flag of Guyana with its correct colors. Give the meaning of the colors and symbols on the flag.

   _____

   _____

   _____

   _____

   _____

   _____

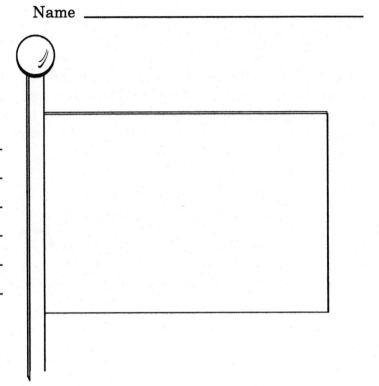

2. Fill in the chart below with the names of three of the earliest known groups of Indians found in Guyana and three groups of Europeans that have shown an interest in Guyana.

Indians	Europeans

3. In 1814, the _____ gained control of Guyana and called it _____

   _____ . After many years of political and racial unrest, Guyana finally

   gained its independence in _____ .

4. Explain how the following people were associated with Guyana's history.

   Cheddi B. Jagan _____

   _____

   Forbes Burnham _____

   _____

   Hugh Desmond Hoyte _____

   _____

   Jim Jones _____

   _____

Name _____

Map Activity

Make a pictorial map of Guyana. Draw and color a variety of different pictures on the map that relate to the country of Guyana. These pictures might include animals, plants, crops, places of interest, famous people, etc. Include at least 12 different topics. Include a key on the bottom of your map that explains what your pictures represent.

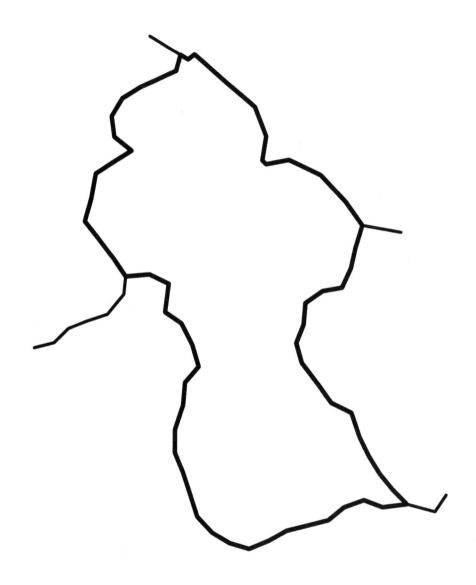

Key

Name _____

Physical Features

1. On the map, draw a star to mark the location of the capital of Paraguay. Write the name nearby.

2. On the map, label the countries that border Paraguay.

3. Paraguay is a landlocked country. Landlocked means

   _____

   _____

   _____ .

4. The _____
   River creates the border between Paraguay and Argentina. Mark this river in blue on the map and label it.

5. The _____
   River divides the country into two major regions. Use green to draw and label this river on the map.

6. Describe Paraguay's two land regions.

   The Chaco _____

   _____

   _____

   Eastern Paraguay _____

   _____

   _____

7. *Quebracho* trees grow in Paraguay and are used in tanning leather. On another paper, explain how this tree is used in the leather-making process. Then illustrate the steps of this process.

History

Name _____

1. Color the flag of Paraguay with its correct colors.

2. Why is the design of Paraguay's flag considered unusual?

_____

_____

_____

_____

3. _____ were the first people to live in Paraguay.

4. _____ and _____ explorers were the first whites to arrive in Paraguay. They were searching for

_____ .

5. Missionaries of the _____ order came to Paraguay in 1588 to convert the Guaraní to _____ . They formed mission settlements called _____ , where the Indians lived and worked.

6. Today, both _____ and _____ are languages spoken in Paraguay.

7. _____ was the first Spanish settlement in Paraguay and is now the country's capital.

8. In the year _____ , Paraguayans overthrew the Spanish governor and declared their independence.

9. For a time, rival political groups struggled for power. Paraguay had more than _____ presidents from 1870 to 1932.

10. Why did Paraguay go to war with Bolivia? What was the result of that war?

_____

_____

_____

_____

Jesuit Reductions

Name _____

Purpose for reading: read the following description as a class. Define *Jesuit, slavery, missionary,* and *colonist.*

Gold and silver were not found in Paraguay, so the Spanish and Portuguese showed little interest in this country. However, in 1609, both governments gave permission to the Jesuits to send Christian missionaries to Paraguay. The Jesuit priests quickly began creating small religious communities known as *reductions,* or *reducciones.*

Reduction means the "gathering together" of people. In this case, the Guaraní Indians were "gathered" by the priests. The Jesuit priests brought the Indians into self-sufficient communities to teach them Christianity, to bring European culture to them, and to protect them from other European colonists and explorers. Slave trading was common. South American native people were often captured by Spanish and Portuguese colonists and sold into slavery, even though it was illegal.

Each reduction consisted of approximately 4,000 Guaraní with two or three Jesuit leaders. Paraguay had 30 such reductions. Under the Jesuits, the Guaraní learned advanced agricultural techniques and grew crops of sugarcane, cotton, rice, tobacco, and wheat. The Guaraní were taught the Christian religion as well as the skills of carpentry, masonry, blacksmithing, and woodworking. The Guaraní also learned about painting, sculpture, calligraphy, and music from the priests.

In 1767, the Jesuits were expelled from Paraguay. The reductions fell into ruin, leaving over 100,000 Indians to fend for themselves. Some Indians returned to the depths of the Chaco and some worked on the estates of Spanish colonists. Others fled to the cities, and others were caught and enslaved or died.

• Divide the class into two factions. Each group should prepare for a debate. Three people should be chosen from each group to represent that group in a debate.

• One side will defend the Jesuits and the Reduction way of life. This group will want to focus on the protection provided by the Jesuits, the skills taught, and the chaos that reigned when the Jesuits were expelled.

• The other group will be opposed to the Jesuits and their gathering of the Guaraní Indians. This group will want to concentrate on the idea of slavery and the appropriateness of imposing a different culture and religion on a group of people.

Extension: Students write an opinion paper following the debate answering this question: Did reductions provide a good or bad way of life for the Guaraní? Why?

Name _____

Ñandutí Lace

Ñandutí describes a style of intricate lace unique to Paraguay. It was introduced to Paraguay by the Jesuit priests. Very large lace hangings have been created, and each ñandutí pattern has its own name. In Paraguay, it is customary to tie a band of ñandutí lace around a black cross in remembrance of a deceased friend.

| Nanduti Lace | Italian Lace | Spider web |

Compare and Contrast

In the columns below, use adjectives to compare the two types of lace and the spider web. An adjective may be used for all three, only two, or only one.

_____ _____ _____
_____ _____ _____
_____ _____ _____
_____ _____ _____
_____ _____ _____

Use the three columns below to list the different shapes you find in the drawings above.

_____ _____ _____
_____ _____ _____
_____ _____ _____
_____ _____ _____
_____ _____ _____

Extension: Find a piece of lace. On another piece of paper, use complete sentences to answer the following questions: Where did you find the lace? Is the lace you found similar to those drawn above? How could this lace be used?

Name _____

Itaipú Dam

The Itaipú Dam on the Paraná River on the Paraguay-Brazil border is one of the largest hydro-electric power projects in the world. *Hydro* is the Greek word for water. A hydro-electric dam generates electricity by using water power and is built across riverbeds. The water is trapped on the upstream side of the dam, forming a reservoir on one side. Power is generated by water forced into huge wheels located under the dam. These huge wheels are called turbines. The turbines are turned by the enormous force of the water and drive another machine called a generator which produces electricity. The water acts as a powerful force because it is under tremendous pressure.

Background for Experiment:

Deep water is under greater pressure than shallow water. That is one reason why underwater divers have to be careful about rising too quickly to the surface of the water after diving deeply. Their bodies have to adjust to the greater pressure as they dive and must reverse this process as they rise to the surface.

Experiment:

Take five plastic soda bottles. With a permanent ink marker, mark a line at 2" increments up the side of each bottle. Fill the bottles with water. Take the bottles outside and set the first one on the sidewalk. Poke a hole at the highest mark on the bottle. Watch carefully. Use chalk to mark the furthest point the water spouted when the hole was poked. Repeat this by poking holes on each of the lower marks on the remaining bottles. Make sure you put the bottles in the same spot each time before making your hole. Also, make holes approximately the same size. This will insure that your results are accurate.

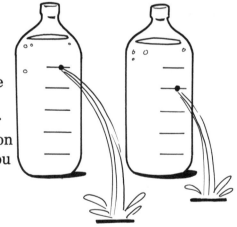

What did you learn about water pressure? _____

_____

_____

_____

_____

_____

Name _____

More About Itaipú Dam

Concrete dams are the strongest of all dams. Still, for a concrete dam to be strong enough to hold an enormous amount of water in a reservoir, the base of the dam has to be built very thickly. On concrete dams, the base's width is roughly ¾ of the height of the dam. For example, if the height of a dam was 80 feet, then the base would be 60 feet thick. Show your math when figuring out the questions below.

• How thick would the base of a concrete dam be if the dam were 144 feet in height?

_____

• How high would a dam be if its base's width were 120 feet? _____

• The Itaipú Dam has 18 turbines. It is capable of generating 12,600 megawatts of power. How many megawatts were generated by one turbine? _____

Extension: Some dams are constructed with rock and clay. A dam like this needs to be very thick. Try building your own dam in a rectangular container using clay, dirt, and rocks to hold it together. Now add water on one side. Does your dam work? Using a knitting needle, punch a small hole in the base of your dam. What happens?

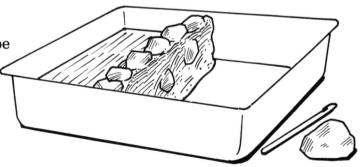

Name _____

The Wars

Read about the following two wars and tell how each affected Paraguay. Be sure to include who the wars were fought against, how long they lasted, and what the results of the wars were. Use complete sentences in your narratives.

War of the Triple Alliance

_____
_____
_____
_____
_____
_____
_____
_____

Chaco War

_____
_____
_____
_____
_____
_____
_____
_____
_____
_____
_____

Name _____

Map Activity

Make a pictorial map of Paraguay. Draw and color a variety of pictures on the map that relate to the country of Paraguay. These pictures might include animals, plants, crops, places of interest, famous people, etc. Include at least 12 different topics. Include a key on the bottom of your map that explains what your pictures represent.

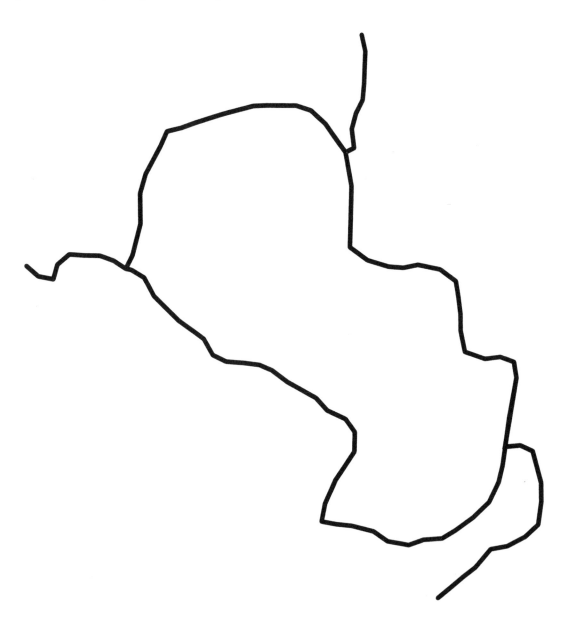

Key

Name _____

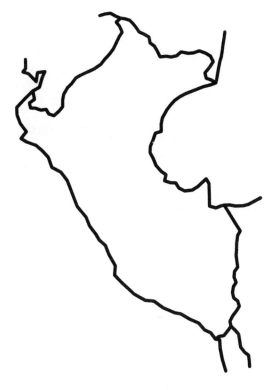

Physical Features

1. On the map, draw a star to mark the location of the capital of Peru. Write the name nearby.

2. Draw and label the mountains in Peru on the map.

3. On the map, label the body of water and the five countries that border Peru.

4. Peru is the third largest country in South America. List the South American countries that are larger than Peru.

   _____

   _____

5. What is the Peru Current? _____

   _____

6. There are three main land regions in Peru. Write a brief description of each of them.

   Coast _____

   _____

   Highlands _____

   _____

   The Selva _____

   _____

   Label and shade in these land regions on the map.

7. Peru's largest lake is _____ . Part of this lake lies in

   _____ .

8. South America's longest river, the _____ River, flows through Peru.

9. Peru _____ lie entirely within the tropics.
   <u>(does, does not)</u>

History

Name _____

1. Color the flag of Peru with its correct colors.

2. Probably the first people to live in Peru

   were _____ who came

   from the continent of _____

   _____ . The

   names of early tribes were

   _____ ,

   _____ ,

   _____ , and

   _____ .

3. What food first grew wild in the highlands of Peru and then was cultivated in Peru as

   well as in many other countries? _____

4. What year did Peru's first constitution go into effect? _____

5. Peru's first president was _____ .

6. Peru lost its valuable _____ deposits as a result of the War of the Pacific.

7. Name two other important dates and events that took place in Peru.

   Date: _____ Event: _____

   _____

   Source: _____ Page(s): _____

   Date: _____ Event: _____

   _____

   Source: _____ Page(s): _____

8. Write a question that you might ask others relating to the history of Peru.

   Question: _____

   Answer: _____

   Source: _____ Page(s)_____

Name _____

Culture and People

1. Write a paragraph about the ruins of Machu Picchu, shown in the picture above.

   _____

   _____

   _____

2. The two official languages of Peru are _____ and

   _____ .

3. What recreational activities do the Peruvians enjoy? Underline the two that you would enjoy most if you lived in Peru.

   _____

   _____

4. Who was Peruvian Ricardo Palma?

   _____

   _____

5. The Indians of Peru make unique arts and crafts. Learn about some of their art works. Draw two or more examples of their work in the box below.

Name _____

Cities of Peru

Arequipa, Calloa, Cusco, and Lima are all cities of Peru. Research two cities of Peru. Write three facts about each of them.

1. City: _____

   Fact: _____

   _____

   Fact: _____

   _____

   Fact: _____

   _____

   Source: _____ Page(s): _____

2. City: _____

   Fact: _____

   _____

   Fact: _____

   _____

   Fact: _____

   _____

   Source: _____ Page(s): _____

Which one of these cities would you prefer to live in if you moved to Peru? Why?

_____

_____

_____

_____

_____

Name _____

Coat of Arms

Find a picture of the Peruvian coat of arms. Draw and color it, including the three symbols that belong on the shield.

What do the three symbols represent?

_____

_____

_____

Source: _____ Page(s): _____

Name _____

Map Activity

Make a pictorial map of Peru. Draw and color a variety of pictures on the map that relate to the country of Peru. These pictures might include animals, plants, crops, places of interest, famous people, etc. Include at least 12 different topics. Include a key on the bottom of your map that explains what your pictures represent.

Key

Name _____

Homes in Peru

Describe different types of homes found in Peru. Then draw and label two of them in the frames below.

_____

_____

_____

_____

Name _____

Fishing in Peru

Peru is a leading fishing country. The main fish that the Peruvians catch in the ocean are anchovies, sardines, and tuna. Research these fish. Note their shapes and colors. Draw these fish as part of an ocean scene below.

Source: _____ Page(s): _____

Source: _____ Page(s): _____

Source: _____ Page(s): _____

Name _____

Physical Features

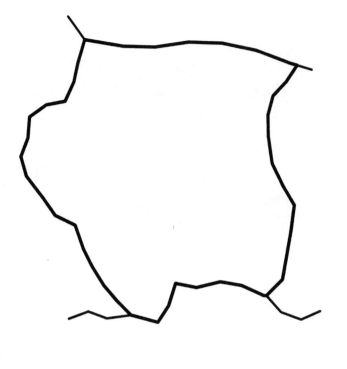

1. On the map, draw a star to mark the location of the capital of Suriname. Write the name nearby.

2. Label the three countries and the body of water that border Suriname.

3. Describe the three land regions found in Suriname.

   narrow coastal area _____

   _____

   _____

   _____

   _____

   mountainous rain forests _____

   _____

   _____

   _____

   savanna _____

   _____

   _____

4. Most of the people live in the _____ area of Suriname.

5. Suriname is the _____ independent country in South America in both
   (smallest, largest)
   area and population.

6. Name the two types of businesses on which the economy of Suriname is based.

   _____   _____

7. Suriname's _____ provide the country's main

   means of transportation.

8. The highest elevation found in Suriname is _____ .

Name _____

General Information

1. List the seven different ethnic groups found throughout Suriname in descending order of population on the ladder.

2. Suriname's official language is

   _____ , but most Suri-

   namese speak _____ .
   This language combines elements of

   _____

   _____

   _____ .

3. Give a general description of the lifestyles of the following groups of people found throughout Suriname:

   Hindustanis _____

   _____

   Creoles _____

   Indonesians _____

   Maroons _____

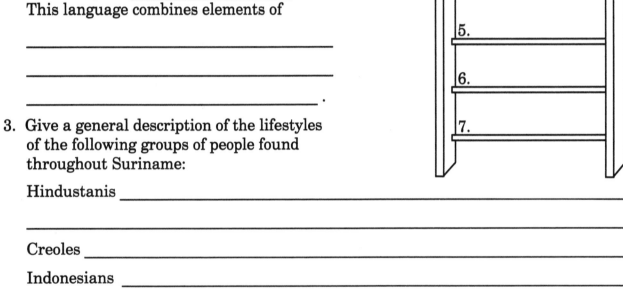

1.
2.
3.
4.
5.
6.
7.

4. Nearly _____ of Suriname's population lives in Paramaribo.
   (half, one-quarter)

5. Name Suriname's three major export products.

   _____   _____   _____

6. _____ is grown on three-fourths of Suriname's farmland.

7. Some other crops grown in Suriname are_____ .

8. The forests of Suriname produce a large quantity of hardwoods that are used for

   _____ and _____ .

9. The basic unit of money in Suriname is the _____ .

Name _____

History

1. Color the flag of Suriname with its correct colors.

2. Name the European countries that owned Suriname during its years of growth and development.

   _____

   _____

3. What did the Dutch give the British in exchange for Suriname in 1667?

   _____

   _____

4. Years of conflict between the different ethnic groups in Suriname delayed its independence until _____.

5. Describe Suriname's National Assembly.

   _____

   _____

   _____

   _____

6. Give another accepted spelling for Suriname. _____

7. Before Suriname became an independent country it was known as

   _____.

8. Before Suriname gained independence, thousands of its people _____

   to the Netherlands. What was the result of this? _____

   _____

   _____

9. Slavery was outlawed in Suriname in _____.

Name _____

City Activity

Research the city of Paramaribo. Write three questions you might ask others relating to this city.

City: Paramaribo

1. Question: _____

   Answer: _____

   Source(s): _____ Page(s):_____

2. Question: _____

   Answer: _____

   Source(s): _____ Page(s):_____

3. Question: _____

   Answer: _____

   Source(s): _____ Page(s):_____

Draw a picture or map of a typical neighborhood in Paramaribo. Include people, buildings, streets, a river, and a park. Label each item according to its function in the neighborhood. Then, on another paper, write a short story about life in this neighborhood.

Name _____

Map Activity

Label each of the following on the map.

Rivers:

Kabalebo   Courantyne
Nickerie   Maroni
Coppename   Litani
Saramacca   Lawa
Suriname   Tapanahoni

Lake:
Blommestein Lake

Highest point:
Juliana Top

Draw in these mountain ranges using this symbol ^^^. Label the mountain ranges:

Käyser   Eilerts De Haan
Oranje   Wilhelmina

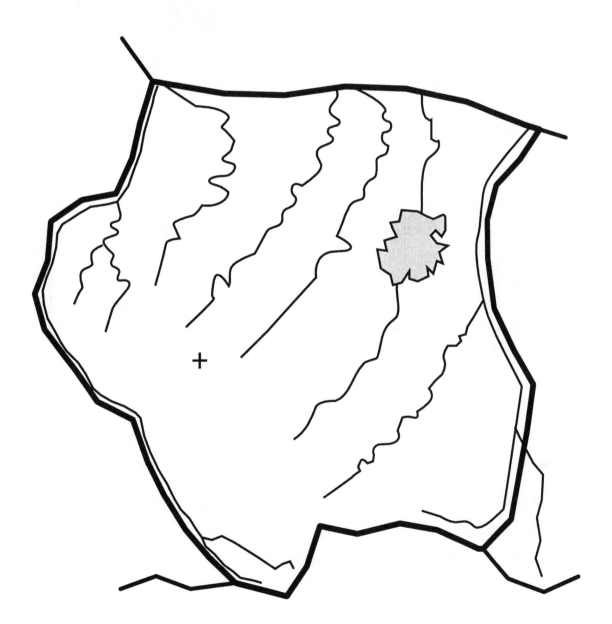

Name _____

Keeping Count of Things in Suriname

Fill in the blanks with the correct number.

1. _____ The percent of Suriname's land that is covered with mountainous rain forests

2. _____ The area of Suriname in square miles

3. _____ The elevation in feet of Mt. Juliana Top

4. _____ The percent of the people between ages 15 and 59 who can read

5. _____ The percentage of exports accounted for by raw bauxite and aluminum

6. _____ The miles of roads

7. _____ The average annual rain fall in west Suriname

8. _____ The average annual rain fall in the Paramaribo area

9. _____ The average annual temperature

10. _____ The estimated population

• Take a count of the following things that pertain to where you live.

1. Your city/town's population: _____

2. The total area of your state or province in square miles: _____

3. The average temperature: winter _____   spring _____

summer _____   fall _____

4. The elevation of the highest point in your state or province: _____

5. The elevation of the lowest point in your state or province: _____

Physical Features

1. On the map, draw a star to mark the location of the capital of Uruguay. Write the name nearby.

2. Label the countries and the body of water that border Uruguay.

3. The _____ River forms a boundary between Uruguay and Argentina. Using blue, mark and label this river on the map.

4. Uruguay has an area of _____ square miles. The interior lowlands make up about four-fifths of Uruguay's land area. Use the space below to figure about how many square miles are taken up by the lowlands.

   About _____ square miles

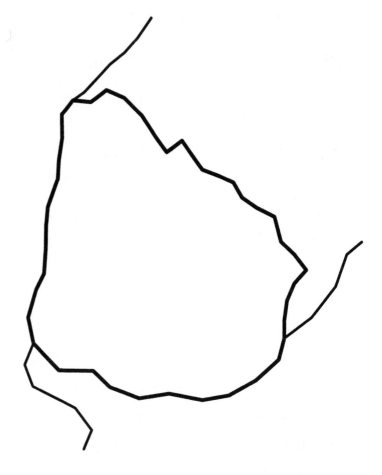

5. The remainder of Uruguay's land covers approximately _____ square miles and makes up the area known as the coastal plains. Use the space below to figure your answer.

6. Show the location of Lake Rincón del Bonete in a color of your choice on the map. It is Uruguay's only large lake. Did this lake always exist? If so, when was it discovered by Europeans? If not, how and when did it come into existence?

   _____

   _____

History

Name _____

1. Color the flag of Uruguay with its correct colors.

2. Match each of the following flag and coat of arms symbols with what they represent by drawing a line from each symbol to its meaning.

Symbol	**Meaning**
Stripes	Liberty and plenty
Scales	Strength
Horse and ox	Justice and equality
Hill of Montevideo	Uruguay's independence
Sun	The way the country was originally divided

3. Read about Uruguay's history. Place the correct date next to each event listed below.

   A. Charrúa Indians, largest group in Uruguay ___*pre–1516*___

   B. *Nova Colonia do Sacramento* established _____

   C. Spaniards settle most of Uruguay _____

   D. Spanish colonists establish Montevideo _____

   E. Portuguese annex Uruguay to Brazil _____

   F. Juan Díaz de Solís lands in Uruguay _____

   G. Uruguay adopts its first constitution _____

   H. José Batlle y Ordóñez elected President _____

4. Place each letter from question #3 at the correct point on the time line. The first one has been done for you.

   A
   |_____|_____|_____|_____|_____|_____|_____|_____|
   1500   1550   1600   1650   1700   1750   1800   1850   1900

5. In what year did Uruguay become a charter member of the United Nations? _____

6. During the early 1980s, thousands of Uruguayans took part in _____ protests. Negotiations between leaders of military and political parties led to _____ elections in 1984 and the formation of a _____ government rather than a _____ one.

Name _____

Uruguayan Leader

One man was particularly influential in making Uruguay of the early 1900s a model of democracy: José Batlle. Read about Batlle. Write notes about Batlle in the spaces below.

My notes about Batlle:

_____

_____

_____

_____

_____

_____

_____

_____

_____

_____

_____

_____

_____

• Write how you think Uruguay would be different today if Batlle had not existed.

_____

_____

_____

_____

_____

_____

_____

_____

_____

_____

Name _____

Montevideo

It is said that all roads in Uruguay lead to Montevideo, its largest city. Montevideo houses 40% of Uruguay's population. Montevideo's historic district, called the "Old Town," has many buildings from the 18th and 19th century. Montevideo is a busy, attractive port city.

Here is a partial map of Montevideo. Below it are various attractions with descriptions of where they can be found in the city. Place the correct corresponding number in each box on the map to show the location of the attraction.

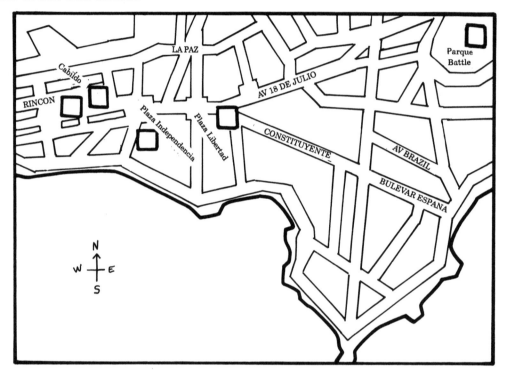

1. **Centenario Stadium**—Scene of Uruguay's major soccer matches. Located in the east side of Parque Batlle.

2. **Museum of Natural History**—Has a collection of fauna, flora, and archeological artifacts of Uruguay. Located on the west side of Plaza Independencia and southeast of the Cathedral.

3. **Cabildo Building**—Place where Uruguay's constitution of 1830 was signed. Located north of Avenida 18 de Julio, just west of Plaza Independencia.

4. **Pre-Colombian & Colonial Arts Museums**—Indian art from all over South America. Located on the northeast corner on Plaza Libertad.

5. **Cathedral**—Example of old architecture. Catholic Church. Located west of Cabildo on the south side of Rincon.

Which of these sights would you be interested in visiting? Why? _____

_____

Name _____

The Gaucho

The gaucho is the Uruguayan version of the American cowboy. During the mid-18th to the mid-19th century, gauchos followed cattle which grazed on Uruguay's rich grasslands. These wanderers followed the herds, bringing them in for sale, living on the range, and eating cattle to survive.

The gaucho has been romanticized in South American literature. For example, in 1872 José Hernández, an Argentinian, wrote the epic poem "El gaucho Martín Fierro," which describes a gaucho and his life. The poem is widely read and greatly loved in Uruguay.

Read as much as you can find on the gaucho. Choose one of the following assignments.

1. The gaucho has become a romantic figure in Uruguayan poetry and literature. Write a poem or a fictional story illustrating how gauchos lived. You must create at least two pictures to go with your writing.

2. The gaucho has been compared to the American cowboy. Write a factual report comparing these cattlemen. Be sure to include ways that they are alike and ways that they are different. Your report should include a drawing or picture of both a gaucho and a cowboy.

Name _____

The Economy

By South American standards, Uruguay is a
wealthy country. Its small population and low
population growth have helped its people
maintain a fairly high standard of living.
Agriculture is one of Uruguay's major economic activities, especially sheep and cattle
raising. In fact, 80% of the country's land is
used for cattle and sheep estancias. Large
amounts of meat are exported to Europe and
Brazil.

- The world price for beef is important to
  Uruguay's economy. Read about Uruguay's
  economy. Write notes about it here. Discuss
  as a class, how this economy differs from or is
  similar to that of your own country.

_____

_____

_____

_____

_____

_____

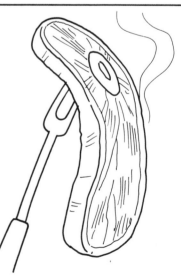

- Now do this research project. You have $250,000 to invest in Uru-
  guayan beef. Use the world price chart for beef in a current newspaper. How many pounds of beef can you purchase with your

  money?_____

  Using the chart on page 91, keep track of world beef prices to determine if you are making or losing money. This financial activity
  should take at least three weeks. Think about how the farmers of
  Uruguay are profiting.

  On the last day, sell your beef and convert the American dollars into
  Uruguayan money using an exchange chart in a current newspaper.

Name _____

The Economy (Cont.)

Date	World Price for Beef	Pounds of Beef	Current Value

Was this a good or a bad investment? _____

Which would have been the best date to sell your beef? _____

Name _____

Map Activity

Make a pictorial map of Uruguay. Draw and color a variety of pictures on the map that relate to the country of Uruguay. These pictures might include animals, plants, crops, places of interest, famous people, etc. Include at least 12 different topics. Include a key on the bottom of your map that explains what your pictures represent.

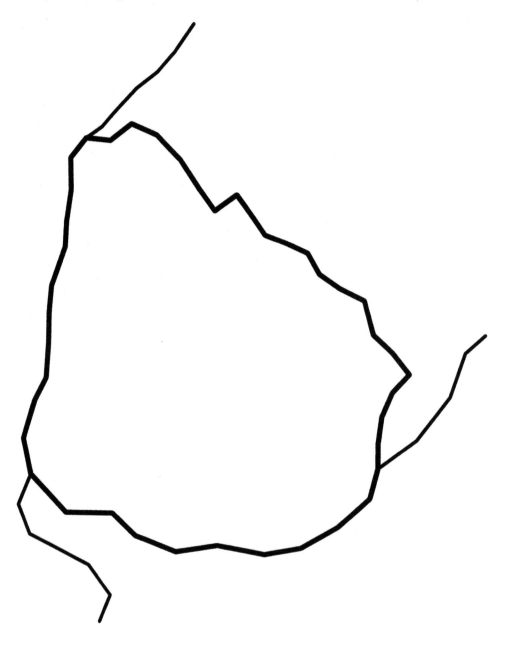

Key

Physical Features

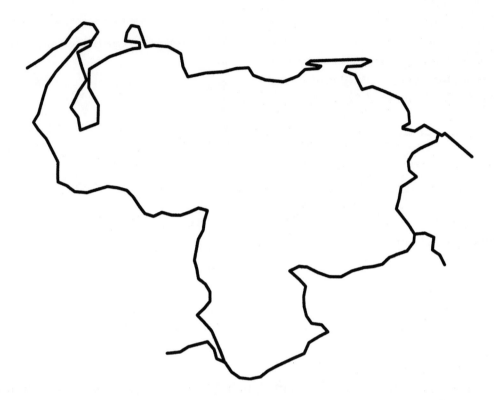

1. On the map, draw a star to mark the location of the capital of Venezuela. Write the name nearby.

2. Label the countries and bodies of water that border Venezuela.

3. Draw the boundaries of the four major land regions of Venezuela on the map. Label these regions. Describe each region below.

   The Maracaibo Basin _____

   _____

   The Andean Highlands _____

   _____

   The Llanos _____

   _____

   The Guiana Highlands _____

   _____

4. Label Lake Maracaibo on the above map. This is the largest lake in South America

   and covers _____ square miles, or _____ square kilometers.

History

Name _____

1. Color the flag of Venezuela with its correct colors.

2. What caused Venezuela to become one of the wealthiest and most rapidly changing countries in South America?

   _____

   _____

   _____

   _____

3. Indian tribes lived in what is now called Venezuela before settlers from Europe arrived. The chief tribes were from two

   groups, the _____ and the _____ . Both

   groups made their livings by _____ , hunting, fishing, and gathering wild plants.

4. Venezuela was the first Spanish colony in South America to proclaim its independence.

   Venezuela declared itself independent on _____ .

   Venezuela was recognized as independent in the year _____ .

5. After achieving independence, Venezuela had many years of unrest due to . . .

   _____

   _____

6. Two dictatorial *caudillos* (leaders) had great influence on Venezuela. Briefly describe the rule of each man.

   Guzmán Blanco _____

   _____

   Juan Vicente Gómez _____

   _____

7. When the worldwide demand for petroleum decreased in the early 1980s, Venezuela's economy, based mainly on oil exports, was hit hard. What has the Venezuelan government done to lower the country's economic dependence on oil?

   _____

   _____

Name _____

Culture and People

1. What would you do if you were a *llaneros* in Venezuela?

   _____

   _____

2. Venezuela has a population of about

   _____ people.

3. About _____ percent of the people live

   in rural areas and about _____
   percent live in cities and towns.

4. Though it is not the country's official religion, most Venezuelans are

   _____ .

5. The official language of Venezuela is _____ .

6. The national dish of Venezuela is called _____ .

   Served mainly at Christmas, it consists of _____ filled

   with a variety of foods and cooked in banana leaf wrappers.

7. Write a brief description of the dancing in Venezuela.

   _____

   _____

8. The most popular spectator sports in Venezuela are _____

   and _____ .

9. Two famous abstract artists of the 1900s are _____

   and _____ . Choose one of the artists. Find photographs and
   information about that artist's work. As an art critic, write about the artist's work and your
   opinion of it.

   _____

   _____

   _____

   _____

   _____

Name _____

Cities in Venezuela

Read about the following four cities. Then write three facts about each of them.

Barquisimeto

1. _____

_____

2. _____

_____

3. _____

_____

Caracas

1. _____

_____

2. _____

_____

3. _____

_____

Ciudad Bolívar

1. _____

_____

2. _____

_____

3. _____

_____

Maracaibo

1. _____

_____

2. _____

_____

3. _____

_____

Name _____

Acrostic Poem

Write a word or phrase about Venezuela using each of the letters in the word Venezuela to make an acrostic poem. Each letter does not have to begin a line of the poem; it can be found anywhere within the line. Draw pictures about the poem around the edge of the paper.

V
E
N
E
Z
U
E
L
A

Name _____

A Letter About Venezuela

You have just spent a week in Venezuela. Write a letter to a friend or relative about the highlights of your trip.

Name _____

Chief Products of Venezuela

List and draw the chief products of Venezuela. If you don't know what something is, consult an encyclopedia or dictionary so you will know how to draw it.

Agriculture:

Manufacturing:

Mining:

Name _____

Map Activity

Make a pictorial map of Venezuela. Draw and color a variety of pictures on the map that relate to the country of Venezuela. These pictures might include animals, plants, crops, places of interest, famous people, etc. Include at least 12 different topics. Include a key on the bottom of your map that explains what your pictures represent.

Key

Name _____

General Information

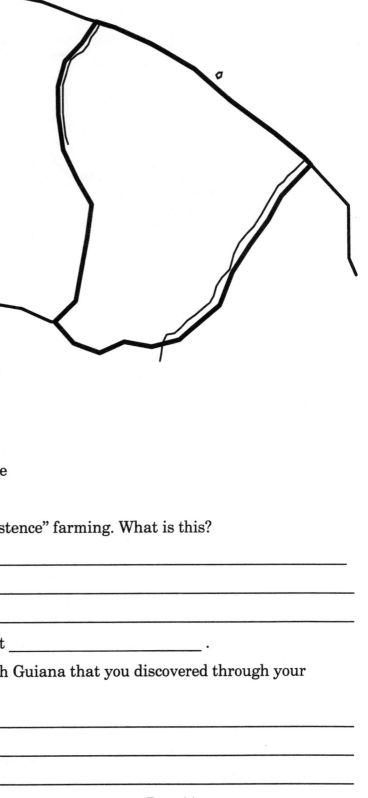

1. On the map, draw a star to mark the location of the capital of French Guiana. Write the name nearby.

2. Write the names of the countries and the body of water that border French Guiana.

3. The city of _____ is the largest city in French Guiana.

4. On the map, label the Maroni River and the Oyapock River, the most important rivers of French Guiana.

5. French Guiana was made an overseas

   department of _____

   in the year _____ .

6. Since farmers are unable to raise enough food for the people of French Guiana, much of the food has to be

   _____ .

7. The _____ of the
   (exterior, interior)
   country is largely uninhabited.

8. Most farming in French Guiana is "subsistence" farming. What is this?

   _____

   _____

   _____

9. The population of French Guiana is about _____ .

10. Write three interesting facts about French Guiana that you discovered through your readings.

    _____

    _____

    _____

Source: _____ Page(s) _____

Falkland Islands
(FAWK-lund)

Name _____

General Information

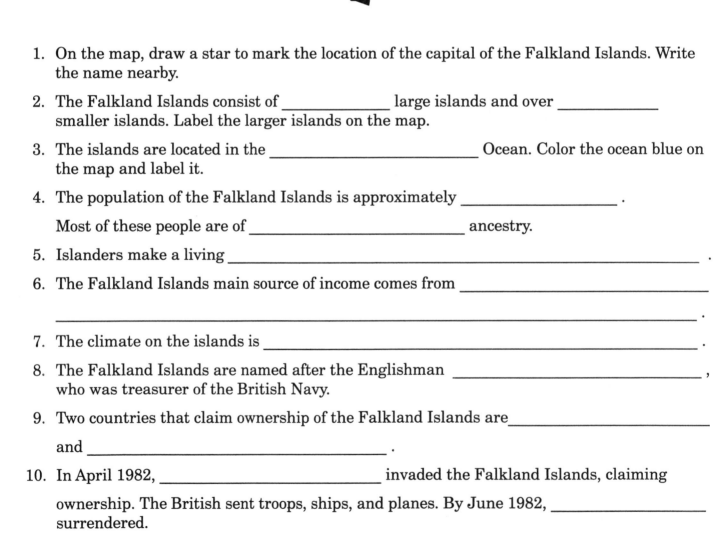

1. On the map, draw a star to mark the location of the capital of the Falkland Islands. Write the name nearby.

2. The Falkland Islands consist of _____ large islands and over _____ smaller islands. Label the larger islands on the map.

3. The islands are located in the _____ Ocean. Color the ocean blue on the map and label it.

4. The population of the Falkland Islands is approximately _____ .

   Most of these people are of _____ ancestry.

5. Islanders make a living _____ .

6. The Falkland Islands main source of income comes from _____

   _____ .

7. The climate on the islands is _____ .

8. The Falkland Islands are named after the Englishman _____ ,
   who was treasurer of the British Navy.

9. Two countries that claim ownership of the Falkland Islands are_____

   and _____ .

10. In April 1982, _____ invaded the Falkland Islands, claiming

    ownership. The British sent troops, ships, and planes. By June 1982, _____
    surrendered.

Answer Key
South America

Overview of South America

Name _____

On the map below label a.) the twelve countries of South America, b.) its two foreign dependencies, c.) all capital cities, d.) the surrounding bodies of water.

© Instructional Fair, Inc.　　　　2　　　　IF8799 South America

Page 2

Overview of South America

Name _____

1. South America is the **four**th largest continent in area.

2. There are many different kinds of landscapes and climates found in South America. Tell where each of the following landscapes/climates can be found in South America.
   World's largest tropical rain forest **Amazon River Basin**
   Rolling grasslands **Argentina　　Venezuela**
   One of the driest places in the world **Atacama Desert**
   Snow-capped mountains and active volcanos **Andes Mountains**

3. Describe each of these main land regions found in South America.
   Andes Mountains **Descriptions will vary.**
   _____
   The Central Plains _____
   _____
   The Eastern Highlands _____
   _____

4. Describe each of the five major river systems found in South America.
   The Amazon River **Descriptions will vary.**
   _____
   The Río de la Plata _____
   The Magdalena and Cauca Rivers _____
   The Orinoco River _____
   The São Francisco River _____
   _____

© Instructional Fair, Inc.　　　　3　　　　IF8799 South America

Page 3

Overview of South America
(Cont.)

Name _____

5. South America has many waterfalls and lakes. Give the location of each of the following and tell one fact about each.　　**Facts will vary.**
   Angel Falls **eastern Venezuela**

   Cuquenán Falls **southeast Venezuela**

   Iguacu Falls **on border of Argentina and Brazil**

   Lake Maracaibo **Venezuela**

   Lake Titicaca **in Andes between Bolivia and Peru**

6. Although South America has a long coastline it has few natural harbors or bays.
   The best natural harbor is found at **Rio de Janeiro**.

7. List four groups of islands that are part of South America.
   Tierra del Fuego Islands
   Juan Fernández Islands
   Falkland Islands
   Galapagos Islands

8. South America's hottest weather conditions are found in Argentina's **Gran Chaco**.
   The temperature reaches **110** °F there.

9. Name the South American countries through which the equator passes.
   Ecuador　Colombia　Brazil

10. Name the highest and lowest places in South America. Give their locations and altitudes.
    Highest **Aconcagua　22,831 ft. above sea level (6959m); in Argentina**
    Lowest **Valdes Peninsula　131 ft. below sea level (40 m); in Argentina**

© Instructional Fair, Inc.　　　　4　　　　IF8799 South America

Page 4

Overview of South America

(Cont.)   Name _____

11. Most South American countries have not fully developed the large amounts of natural resources found within their boundaries and therefore have a low standard of living. Name the four countries that have the most developed economies.

Argentina _____ Brazil _____
Uruguay _____ Venezuela _____

12. Describe the differences between small and large farms in South America.

Answer might include... small farms are only big enough to grow food for a family and are usually rented; the large farms are prosperous and use modern methods and equipment

13. List seven valuable export crops that are grown in South America.

bananas _____ beef _____ coffee _____ grains
soybeans _____ sugar _____ wool

14. Some farmers grow Marijuana or coca for the international trade in illegal drugs. Authorities think that in Bolivia, Colombia, and Peru the value of these drug exports is higher (higher, lower) than the value of all other export crops.

15. Approximately one-fourth of the world's coffee is grown in the South American country of Brazil. Colombia is another South American country that is a very large coffee producer.

16. Brazil is South America's leading manufacturing country. Name five products that are produced in this country.

vehicles _____ computers _____ televisions
light aircraft _____ weapons

17. Tell what kind of mining is found in each of the countries listed below.

Venezuela petroleum, iron ore
Bolivia tin
Chile copper, sodium nitrate
Peru oil, copper, lead, zinc
Columbia oil, emeralds, coal
Ecuador oil

Page 5

Overview of South America

(Cont.)   Name _____

18. Name the softwood whose timber is Brazil's chief forest product.

Parana pine
Tell how it is used. Used in construction industry to make concrete molds

19. List other products Brazil's forests yield.

Answers may include: waxes, fibers, gums, resins, nuts, medicines, rubber, oils

20. Describe the fishing industry of Chile and Peru including the work of the fishing fleets and how their catch is used.

Descriptions will vary. Might include large catches of anchovettas and fish that are made into oil and fish meal

21. On what continents are South America's leading trade partners located?

North America, Europe

22. Do ships or do trains play a large role in South America's transportation of goods?

Ships

23. Explain what kinds of transportation the people in poor, rural areas of South America use.

Burros and llamas which carry loads; oxen and horses to pull carts

24. Radio and television are especially valued as sources of information because many of the people cannot read or write.

25. The Galapagos Islands belong to Ecuador and are known for being the home of giant turtles that weigh more than 500 pounds.

Page 6

Overview of South America

(Cont.) Descriptions will vary. Name _____

26. Describe the following animals and plants that can be found in South America.

capybara world's largest rodent; 4 ft. long
pirarucú large river fish - more than 7 ft. long + 200 lbs.
tapir large, wild hoglike animal
piranha small fish that eats flesh
vicuaña and guanaco wild members of camel family
anaconda large snake; up to 30 ft. long
cacao tree beans used to make cocoa and chocolate
sisal plant Its fibers are used for making twine.
coca shrub leaves are a source for drugs, such as cocaine
cinchona tree provides quinine
quebracho tree provides tannin

27. Define the phrase "domesticated animal." Name two animals that are believed to have been domesticated in South America and tell why they are important to the people of South America. Draw and label a picture of each animal in one of the boxes below.

A domesticated animal is an animal adapted for human use.

1. alpaca - its wool is useful

2. llama - used as a transport animal

Student draws picture here.

Student draws picture here.

Page 7

South American Land Regions

Name _____

Color the area on the map that shows the location of each of the following kinds of land regions: Andes Mountains - brown; Eastern Highlands - green; Central Plains - yellow.

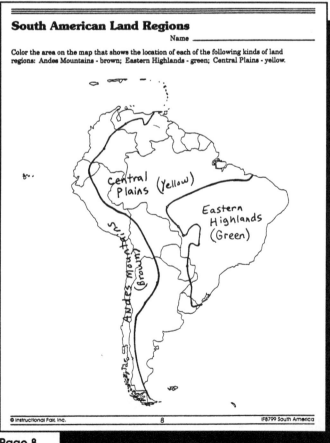

Central Plains (Yellow)
Eastern Highlands (Green)
Andes Mountains (Brown)

Page 8

Physical Features

Name _____

1. On the map, draw a star to mark the location of the capital of Argentina. Write the name nearby.

2. On the map, label the five countries and the body of water that border Argentina.

3. Use the symbol ᨊ to show the location of the Andes Mountains in Argentina on the map.

4. There are four major land regions in Argentina. Some contain subregions. Write a brief description of each.

Northern Argentina: _Descriptions will vary._

The Gran Chaco _____

Mesopotamia _____

Pampa: _____

The Andine: _____

Andes Mountain _____

The Piedmont _____

Patagonia: _____

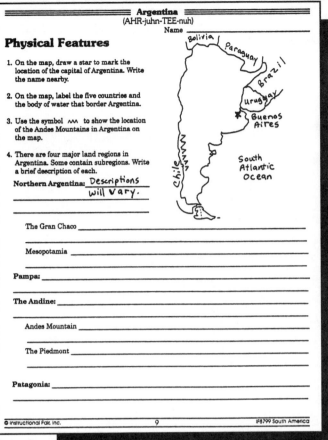

Bolivia
Paraguay
Brazil
Uruguay
★ Buenos Aires
Chile
South Atlantic Ocean

Page 9

Name _____

Physical Features (Cont.)

5. Describe the natural phenomena that occurs near the junction of the Iguaça and Paraná Rivers.
   The Iguaça Falls are formed. Descriptions will vary.

6. The island located on the southern tip of South America that belongs to both Chile and Argentina is called _Tierra del Fuego_. This island is separated from the mainland of South America by the _Strait of Magellan_.

7. The highest point in Argentina is _Aconcagua_. It is _22,831_ feet above sea level. The lowest point in Argentina is _Valdés Peninsula_. It is _131_ feet below sea level.

8. Name the months in which Argentina's winter and summer take place.
   December to March - Summer; June to September - winter

9. Describe how winds from the oceans affect Argentina's climate.
   Descriptions will vary. Moist air from the Atlantic can make summers very humid in mesopotamia and the Pampa. Winds warm plateau in winter; cool it in summer. Wind from Antarctica brings snow.

10. Name the land features which attract recreation-seekers to Argentina. Then, in the box below, draw a picture of one of the activities you would like to do.
    sandy beaches along coast, rugged mountains, hill country

Page 10

Culture and People

Name _____

1. Explain the meaning of the sun and cap on the coat of arms of Argentina.
   Sun - freedom from Spain
   Cap - liberty

2. People of _European_ ancestry make up about 85 percent of Argentina's people.

3. Mestizos are people of mixed _Indian_ and _White_ ancestry. Mestizos make up about 15 percent of Argentina's population.

4. The official language of Argentina is _Spanish_.

5. Name the metropolitan area in which about 11 million Argentines live. _Greater Buenos Aires_

6. About 88 percent of Argentina's people reside in _cities_ or _towns_.

7. Much of the Pampa and Patagonia is covered with ranches called _estancias_.

8. The national drink of the people of Argentina is a tea called _maté_, which is a blend of dried leaves from the native _holly_ tree.

9. The main religion practiced in Argentina is _Catholicism_.

10. Explain why the original Indian population of Argentina declined. _Answer might include illnesses brought by Europeans and intermarriage with Europeans_

11. Most Argentines make what kind of meat the main part of many meals? _beef_

12. Argentina's most loved sport is _soccer_. Another popular sport is *pato*. In this game, riders on _horseback_ try to throw a six-handled _ball_ into a _basket_.

13. _The University of Buenos Aires_ is the biggest university in South America.

Page 11

History

Name _____

1. Color the flag of Argentina with its correct colors. Write the meaning of the colors and symbols found on the flag on the lines below.
   Blue and white to represent the patriots who fought off Britain in 1806 and 1807; the sun equals freedom from Spain.

2. The first European settlers to arrive in Argentina in the early 1500s were the _Spanish_, who ruled for 300 years.

3. Explain how the establishment of a Portuguese trading post in 1680 influenced the growth of the Spanish colony in Argentina.
   When the Portuguese set up the post across the Río de la Plata from Buenos Aires, the Spanish government decided to develop Argentina in order to protects its investment and territory.

4. Identify the Sáenz Peña Law. _A law that established a secret ballot voting system and the registration for military service_

5. Identify the following dates important to Argentina's history.
   1853: _National government with a Constitution_
   1860: _Argentina officially named_
   1930: _Army officers overthrew elected government_
   1946: _Perón elected president of Argentina_

Page 12

Who's Who In Argentina

Name _____

Many outstanding people have made significant contributions to Argentina's growth and development. Identify each of the following influential people.

Answers will vary. Might include these facts:

José de San Martín ___Led fight for independence from Spain in 1812.___

Juan Perón ___Overthrew military dictatorship.___

Carlos Saúl Menem ___Took over leadership of Argentina in 1989.___

Alberto Ginastera ___classical composer___

Alicia Peñalba ___sculptor___

Prilidiano Pueyrredón ___painter___

José Hernández ___Poet who wrote about rebellious cowboys___

Domingo Faustino Sarmiento ___Author who wrote about importance of education as a way for Argentina to grow___

Page 13

Map Activity

Name _____

Make a pictorial map of Argentina. Draw and color a variety of pictures on the map that relate to the country of Argentina. These pictures might include animals, plants, crops, places of interest, famous people, etc. Include at least twelve different topics. Include a key on the bottom of your map that explains what your pictures represent.

Pictures will vary.

Key

Page 14

Cities to Know About

Name _____

Choose two of the following cities and write three questions that you might ask others relating to that city.

Buenos Aires   Córdoba   Mar del Plata
Paraná   Rosario   Santa Fe
Tucumán

Answers will vary.

City: _____
1. Question: _____
   Answer: _____
   Source(s) _____ Page(s): _____
2. Question: _____
   Answer: _____
   Source(s): _____ Page(s): _____
3. Question: _____
   Answer: _____
   Source(s): _____ Page(s): _____

City: _____
1. Question: _____
   Answer: _____
   Source(s): _____ Page(s): _____
2. Question: _____
   Answer: _____
   Source(s): _____ Page(s): _____
3. Question: _____
   Answer: _____
   Source(s): _____ Page(s): _____

Page 15

A Proud Heritage

Name _____

Read about Argentina's gauchos. Write a brief paragraph describing who they are, where they live, and what they do. Then draw a picture of a gaucho and label the different parts of his unique clothing.

Answers will vary.

Page 16

Page 17

Spanish Words to Know

Spanish is the official language in Argentina, though many Argentines also speak a second European language.

Match the Spanish word with the correct definition. Not all definitions will be used.

D mestizos   A. a kind of stew

G porteños   B. a horseback game in which two teams of riders try to grab a six-handled ball, carry it downfield, and toss it into a basket

J estancias   C. cowboy

H poncho   D. people of mixed Indian and European ancestry

B pato   E. a cord-and-weight sling thrown to entangle the legs of the animal being hunted

F asado con cuero   F. a barbecue at which beef is roasted in its hide over an open fire

A pucheros   G. people of the port

E bola   H. a blanket with a slit in the middle for the head

    I. pastries stuffed with meat or fish, eggs, fruits, and vegetables

    J. large ranches

Write three other Spanish words and a definition for each.

1. _____ Answers will vary. _____
2. _____
3. _____

Write a paragraph in English, but incorporate the three Spanish words from above.

_____ Paragraphs will vary. _____

Page 17

Page 18

Physical Features

1. On the map, draw stars to mark the locations of the two capitals of Bolivia. Write the names nearby.

2. On the map, label the countries that border Bolivia.

3. Lake _Titicaca_ is located on the border of Bolivia and Peru. Color this lake blue on the map. This is the world's highest navigable lake.

Navigable means _able to be sailed on or through_ .

4. Use ∧∧∧ to show the location of the Andes Mountains on the map.

5. Bolivia has four major land regions. Write about one distinctive feature of each region.

The Andean Highlands _Answers will vary._

The Yungas _____

The Valles _____

The Oriente _____

6. Bolivia lies _South_ of the equator. Bolivian seasons are (north, south)

the opposite of the seasons in the northern hemisphere. (the same as, the opposite of)

7. The rainy season in most of Bolivia begins in _December_ and ends in _February_ .

Page 18

Page 19

History

1. Color the state flag of Bolivia with its correct colors.

2. Bolivia's state flag is used only by the government. What is the difference between the "state" flag and the national flag used by the Bolivian people? _There is no coat of arms on the flag used by the people._

3. American Indians have lived in Bolivia for _thousands_ of years. (hundreds, thousands)

4. The _Tiahuanaco_ Indians had a major civilization by Lake Titicaca around A.D. 100. By the late 1300s, the _Aymara_ Indians had taken over the region. These Indians were very war-like. In the 1400s, the _Inca_ Indians of Peru took over the region.

5. In the 1530s, Spain conquered Bolivia and made it a Spanish colony which they called _Upper Peru_ or _Charcas_ .

6. The Spanish discovered the precious metal _silver_ in Bolivia. This became an important source of wealth for Spain.

7. In the 1800s, the country of _Venezuela_ helped Bolivia win its independence from Spain.

8. Bolivia is named for _General Simón Bolívar_, who helped lead the country to independence.

9. How did Bolivia lose over half of its total land area? _through wars or treaties with Argentina, Brazil, Chile, Paraguay, and Peru._

10. Why did Bolivian workers strike often in the 1980s? _To protest rising prices, inadequate wages, and shortages of food._

Page 19

Page 20

Lost Land

On August 6, 1825, Bolivia became an independent republic. When Bolivia gained its independence, it claimed much more land than it does today. During the War of the Pacific (1879–1883), Bolivia lost its land along the Pacific coast to Chile, giving up this land's rich nitrate deposits and its access to the ocean shipping port. Powerful Brazil annexed three sections of Bolivia. Peru gained a small section of Bolivia. In 1932, war broke out between Bolivia and Paraguay over a piece of land. Bolivia lost and signed the land over to Paraguay in 1938.

On the map below, the land Bolivia once claimed is marked with slanted lines. Look at a current political map of Bolivia and the surrounding countries. Then color the land Bolivia lost to Peru with yellow, to Brazil with blue, to Paraguay with red, and to Chile with green. Be sure to add these colors to the key.

| yellow | Peru | red | Paraguay |
| blue | Brazil | green | Chile |

Looking at the map, what percentage of Bolivia's original land do you think was lost?

_____ 10%   _____ 25%   ✓ 50%   _____ 80%

What do you think was Bolivia's most devastating loss of land and why? Answer this question on another paper. Be sure to use complete sentences.

Page 20

Cities of Bolivia

Name _____

La Paz

La Paz is the actual capital of Bolivia. It has the executive and legislative branches of government and is Bolivia's largest city and commercial center. The city is located on the slopes and bottom of a canyon in the *altiplano* (high plateau) region. Peaks of the Andes Mountains tower over the city. About one million people live in La Paz. Adobe and brick homes crouch on the hillsides and skyscrapers rise from the valley depths. A modern residential area is located on the floor of the canyon. Aymaran Indians make up about half of the La Paz population. The city has an open market where people can purchase vegetables, fruit, whole pigs, household goods, and hot, fresh coffee. At 12,000 feet (3660 meters) above sea level, La Paz is the highest capital in the world.

Cochabamba

This city rests in the highly populated, fertile Cochabamba Basin. Its climate is more mild than that of the antiplano region. It sits in a valley at 8,376 feet (2553 meters) above sea level. It has a population of about 317,000. A comfortable climate and attractive setting have helped make Cochabamba the third largest city in Bolivia. A big plaza in the city's center honors the date when local patriots began to fight against Spanish rule in the War of Independence. Travel from Cochabamba to La Paz is possible by air, rail, and highway.

Write the name of the city which most closely fits the phrase.

La Paz	about 1,000,000 people live here
Cochabamba	located in a basin
La Paz	located in the altiplano region
Cochabamba	plaza honoring War of Independence
Cochabamba	mild, comfortable climate
La Paz	highest capital in the world
La Paz	skyscrapers in valley
Cochabamba	About 317,000 people live here
La Paz	modern residential area on canyon floor

Read about Sucre, the official capital of Bolivia. Write a paragraph comparing Sucre to La Paz. Your comparison should include at least one way that these cities are similar and one way that they are different.

Page 21

V.I.B. (Very Important Bolivian)

Name _____

Simón Bolívar was so important to Bolivia that the country is named for him. Bolívar was vital to several South American countries in gaining their independence. Research Simón Bolívar. Below, write about what *you think* of Bolívar and his life. Give specific examples from his life that support what you think. For example, if you admire Bolívar, state that. Then, give specific instances from his life that support your belief that he is an admirable person.

Answers will vary.

Page 22

Women's Clothing

Name _____

Many working-class Bolivians, called *cholos*, wear the clothing of their ancestors. The traditional dress includes a brightly colored skirt with many underskirts, known as a *polleras*. These women also frequently wear a woolen shawl over a blouse. Red is a favorite clothing color. Hair is often worn in two long braids.

A person can learn a lot about a Bolivian woman by the hat she wears. Here are some examples: The Aymará women of La Paz wear black bowler hats. The Campesina women of the Cochabamba valleys wear tall, white hats with black ribbons. The number and form of the loops of ribbons around the crown tell if the wearer is single, married, or a widow. Quechua women of the highlands east of the Altiplano wear flat-topped hats made of white wool. These hats are taller and broader than the Aymará bowler hats.

On the lines provided, name the women who wear each hat and where they live. Then draw a line from each hat to the place on the map where it is worn.

women: Campesina
location: Cochabamba

women: Aymará
location: La Paz

women: Quechua
location: highlands east of Altiplano

Page 23

Mamoré River Trip

Name _____

Locate the cities Guajará-Mirim and Trinidad on a map. Locate the Mamoré River on a map. Then, read the following page from a diary which describes a boat trip down this river from Guajará-Mirim to Trinidad.

Dear Diary,

I am traveling on a cattle boat down the Mamoré River in Bolivia. The boat is a double-decker wooden barge with an old, smoky gasoline engine. The cattle are kept on the lower level, and the passengers ride on the bridge, or upper level. I sleep in a hammock. The sun is hot and intense and the cattle smell bad, but the scenery is beautiful. We travel through thick jungles filled with fantastic birds. I see green and yellow macaws, white egrets and storks. Blue kingfishers swoop into the water and emerge with fish in their beaks. The water is a dirty brown so I am unable to see fish, but I spy the pink dolphin which lives in the Amazon River and many of its tributaries. South American alligators, known as caimans, sunbathe on sandbars we pass. It is the end of the rainy season, so the river is swollen and driftwood and other debris float on the water.

As we pass the villages, the native men paddle their canoes out to our boat to try to sell food and wild animal skins, usually alligator and jaguar. The trip will take six days, but already I feel myself slipping into the rhythm of the river.

Define the following terms:

barge ___ flat-bottomed boat
hammock ___ hanging bed
tributaries ___ smaller streams that flow into a main river
debris ___ ruins, fragments, rubbish
jaguar ___ large cat with spots

Would you like to take a trip like this? Why or why not?

On another paper, create a picture which shows what you think the river and the surrounding landscape looks like. Be sure to include the animals. Look up unfamiliar animals in a reference book so you can include them in your picture.

Page 24

Name _____

Balsa Boats

The people who live in Bolivia on Lake Titicaca, the highest lake in the world, make boats out of dried reeds. The boats are known as balsa boats. The reeds are harvested and laid in the sun to dry. After drying, they are made into tight bundles which form the base and side of the boat. Sometimes a boat has a sail also made from reeds. Boats are removed from the lake when they are not being used. This allows the reeds to dry out between trips and prevents rot.

• Are reeds or grass really good boat building material?

What do you think? Make a guess or hypothesis before you do the following experiment. Then keep notes on the experiment using the chart on page 26.

Materials: Students or teacher gather different grasses and dry them. Grasses should come from wet areas and have different circumferences. Grasses should be harvested whole and a chart made listing the different types of grasses used. (Include the grass head on the chart.) The chart allows students to compare their pieces of grass stem to the actual plant on the chart. You also need wood (sticks or bark). Include whole wood samples on your chart. Margarine tubs, medium–sized rubber bands, and water complete the materials list.

#1 Comparing Grasses: Take a small sample of each of the grasses, approximately 1" in length. Samples may be marked with a permanent marker so students know what sample they have. This can be correlated with same grass types on the chart. Place all samples of grass in a margarine tub (or tubs) filled with water. Each day, record the status of the grasses. Have any sunk? Do they all float? Does the size of the grass stem seem to matter? This experiment should run at least one week, but may be conducted as long as you wish.

#2 Comparing Grass with wood: Wood is also used as a boat-building material. In this experiment, students will compare the floating capabilities of wood versus grass. Conduct this experiment the same way you did #1, but this time add the different types of wood that were collected. Woods that are difficult to distinguish should also be marked with a permanent marker. Which floats longest, grass or wood? The experiment should be conducted until boat materials become saturated and begin to sink.

#3 Weight Experiments/Comparing Grasses: Cut 10 three-inch lengths of each of the grass samples. Make bundles of 10 of each of the like grasses and tie them together with rubber bands. Make sure the rubber band is at the midpoint of the bundle. Rubber bands do not float. Test this yourself. To see how much weight the different grasses can hold, continue to add rubber bands, tightly wrapped, to each bundle. How many rubber bands does it take to sink each bundle? Which bundle held the most weight? Why do you think you got the results you did?

Page 25

Name _____

Balsa Boats Experiment Results

Use for #1 and #2.

Grass or Wood (number or name these)	Observations (How many days does it take for each to sink?)

Use for #3.

Grasses or Wood	Observations (Number of rubber bands it takes to sink.)

Page 26

Name _____

Map Activity

Make a pictorial map of Bolivia. Draw and color a variety of pictures on the map that relate to the country of Bolivia. These pictures might include animals, plants, crops, places of interest, famous people, etc. Include at least 12 different topics. Include a key on the bottom of your map that explains what your pictures represent.

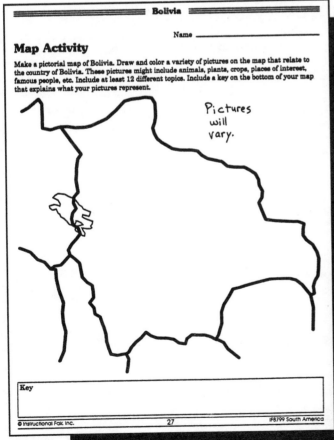

Pictures will vary.

Key

Page 27

Name _____

Physical Features

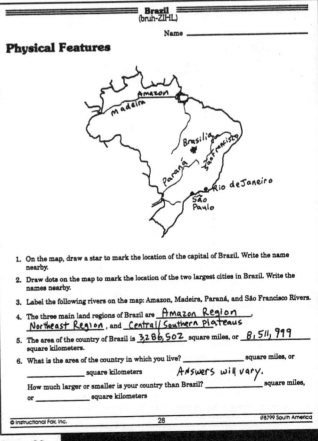

1. On the map, draw a star to mark the location of the capital of Brazil. Write the name nearby.

2. Draw dots on the map to mark the location of the two largest cities in Brazil. Write the names nearby.

3. Label the following rivers on the map: Amazon, Madeira, Paraná, and São Francisco Rivers.

4. The three main land regions of Brazil are ___Amazon Region___, ___Northeast Region___, and ___Central/Southern plateaus___.

5. The area of the country of Brazil is ___3,286,502___ square miles, or ___8,511,999___ square kilometers.

6. What is the area of the country in which you live? _____ square miles, or _____ square kilometers   Answers will vary.

   How much larger or smaller is your country than Brazil? _____ square miles, or _____ square kilometers

Page 28

History

Name _____
(1)

1. Color the Brazilian flag using the correct colors. On the lines below, describe the meaning of each color and write the motto found on the flag.

   Green and golden-yellow represent forests and minerals. Blue and white are Portugal's historic colors. The motto means "Order and Progress."

2. Brazil was named after trees found there known as brazilwoods

3. Brazil has 26 states and 1 federal district. This federal district encompasses Brasília

4. The major Indian groups that lived in Brazil before the Europeans arrived were the Guaraní and Tupinamba.

5. One of the emperors of Brazil, Pedro II, took office at the early age of 15. He helped Brazil progress in many ways. List them below.

   Answers might include new railroads and telegraph lines, modern banking system, textile industry, new schools.

6. Brazil became a republic on Nov. 15, 1889.

Page 29

Culture and People

Name _____

1. Brazil has 6019 miles or 9687 kilometers of coastline. Thousands of people go to the beach to enjoy various kinds of recreation such as Answers might include fishing, skindiving, swimming, and boating.

2. Brazil's number one sport is soccer. Other popular sports are auto racing, basketball, horse racing.

3. Carnival is Brazil's most famous festival. It is celebrated during the four days preceding Lent.

4. Three main ethnic groups make up Brazil's population: whites, blacks, and people of mixed ancestry. The mixed groups include *caboclos*, who are people of mixed white and Indian ancestry and *mulattoes*, who are people of mixed black and white ancestry.

5. Portuguese is the nation's official language, though Indian groups in the Amazon area still speak traditional languages.

6. Government buildings in Brazil are known for their modern architecture. Study some of the government buildings and draw and label one of them in the box below.

Page 30

Cities in Brazil

Name _____

Belém	Manaus	Rio de Janeiro	Santos
Belo Horizonte	Pôrto Alegre	Salvador	São Paulo
Brasília	Recife		

Find the location of each of the cities listed above on a map of Brazil.

Choose one of the above cities in Brazil to study. Write a description of this city to share with others.   Answers will vary.

Name of the city: _____

I chose this city to study because _____

The population of this city was _____ in the year _____.

Write a description of the city.

_____

Page 31

Chief Products of Brazil

Name _____

List the name of a Brazilian product in each category and draw a small picture of it in the space provided. Conduct research in an encyclopedia or dictionary about how that product is produced. Write a description in the space provided.

Answers will vary.

Product	Production Procedures
Agriculture:	
Mining:	
Manufacturing and Processing:	
Forest Products:	

Page 32

Name _____

Animals of the Rain Forest

The Amazon Region occupies most of northern Brazil. It is mostly covered by jungle and tropical rain forest called *selva*. Read and discover what animals live in this region. Below, draw and label at least eight different animals in their rain forest habitat.

Pictures
will
vary.

Page 33

Name _____

Portuguese Language

The official language of Brazil is Portuguese. Find a Portuguese dictionary, an encyclopedia that includes the Portuguese language, or a book on Portuguese. Use the book(s) to help you complete the activities below.

1. Write the correct numbers above the Portuguese words for them.

3	8	4	1
três	oito	quatro	um or uma
10	7	6	9
dez	sete	seis	nove

2. In Portuguese, write the words for the numbers in the correct order. Put a comma between the words to show where each word ends. Write the name of the reference book, including the page number, where you found the information.

   um or uma, três, quatro, seis, sete, oito, nove, dez

   Source: _____ Page(s): _____

3. Draw at least three objects in the box below and label them in English and in Portuguese. You may use the back of this paper if you want to draw and label more objects. It is important that you check to see that you have spelled the words correctly. Learn to say some of the words.

   Source: _____ Page(s): _____

   Answers
   will
   vary.

Page 34

Name _____

Map Activity

Make a pictorial map of Brazil. Draw and color a variety of pictures on the map that relate to the country of Brazil. These pictures might include animals, plants, crops, places of interest, famous people, etc. Include at least 12 different topics. Include a key on the bottom of your map that explains what your pictures represent.

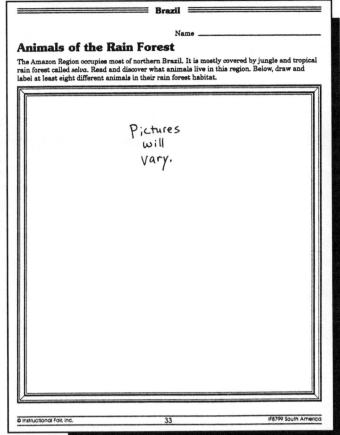

Pictures
will
vary.

Key

Page 35

Name _____

Physical Features

1. On the map, draw a star to mark the location of the capital of Chile. Write the name nearby.

2. On the map, label the three countries and the body of water that border Chile.

3. What are the names of the major islands that belong to Chile?

   Easter Island
   Juan Fernández
   Islands

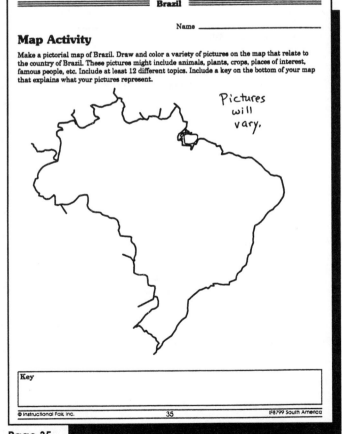

4. Give a brief description of the three land regions of Chile.

   Descriptions will vary.

   The Northern Desert _____
   _____
   _____

   The Central Valley _____
   _____
   _____

   The Archipelago _____
   _____

5. Tell about some of the attractions of the Lake Country area, just south of the Bío-Bío River, which is a popular summer vacation spot.

   lakes, valleys, volcanoes, stunning scenery —
   fishing, boating, hiking

Page 36

Culture and People

Name _____

1. The Chilean coat of arms bears the Spanish words "Por la Razon o la Fuerza" which means . .
   By Right or by Might.
   Color the coat of arms.

2. Most Chileans are a mix of Spanish and Indian ancestry.
   These Chileans follow the Catholic religion and speak Spanish.

3. Name three groups of Indians found in Chile.
   Araucanians, Quechuas, Aymara

4. Describe the different kinds of housing found in Chilean cities.
   Varies from modern high-rise apartments to Spanish-style homes to shacks in slums.

5. Explain why many poor rural Chileans moved to the cities since the 1940s and the result.
   To look for jobs and a better lifestyle. Jobs were scarce and many of the people were unskilled. Many had to take low-paying jobs and live in slums.

6. Name the occupation of most rural Chileans. Farming
   Some work on large farms, owned by the wealthy, as laborers or sharecroppers

7. Chile's most popular spectator sport is soccer.

Page 37

History

Name _____

1. Color the flag of Chile in its correct colors. Give the meaning of the colors/symbols found on the flag.
   Red = blood of heroes
   White = snow of Andes
   Blue = the sky
   White star = progress and honor

2. Fill in the dates of the following historic events that took place in Chile:

late 1400s	Conquered by the Incas.
1533	Spaniards invade and conquer Chile.
1818	Chile gains its independence from Spain.
1836	Chile declares war on Peru and Bolivia to prevent them from uniting.
1925	A constitution established direct elections for the president and the separation of church and state.
1970	Salvador Allende Gossens, a Marxist, elected president.
1989	Democratic type of government established.

3. Explain why the Spaniards began to explore Chile and what they did when they could not find what they were searching for.
   The Spaniards explored Chile in search of gold and silver. When they could not find gold and silver, they stayed and raised cattle and wheat.

4. The first European explorer to reach Chile was Ferdinand Magellan.
5. The founder of Santiago was Pedro de Valdivia.
6. The Irishman who defeated the Spanish in 1817 was Bernado O'Higgins.
7. The 1989 president-elect of Chile was Patricio Aylwin.

Page 38

Map Activity

Name _____

Draw and color a variety of pictures around the map that relate to the country of Chile. These pictures might include animals, plants, crops, places of interest, famous people, etc. Include at least 12 different topics. Include a key on the bottom of your map that explains what your pictures represent.

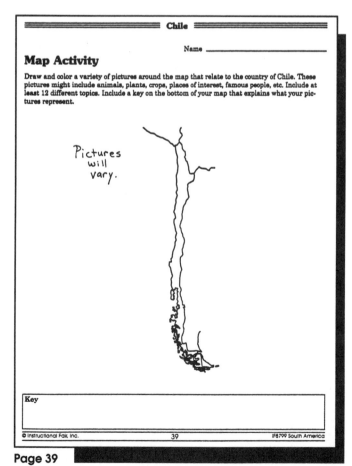

Pictures will vary.

Key

Page 39

Cities to Know About

Name _____

Choose two of the following cities. Research and write three questions that you might ask others relating to each city.

Santiago   Concepción   Valparaíso   Viña del Mar

City: _____ Answers will vary. _____

1. Question: _____
   Answer: _____
   _____
   Source: _____ Page(s): _____
2. Question: _____
   Answer: _____
   _____
   Source: _____ Page(s): _____
3. Question: _____
   Answer: _____
   _____
   Source: _____ Page(s): _____

City: _____

1. Question: _____
   Answer: _____
   _____
   Source: _____ Page(s): _____
2. Question: _____
   Answer: _____
   _____
   Source: _____ Page(s): _____
3. Question: _____
   Answer: _____
   _____
   Source: _____ Page(s): _____

Page 40

Chile

Name _____

Spanish Words to Know

Match the Chilean terms with the correct definitions. Not all definitions will be used.

- **C** callampas
- **D** fundos
- **I** huasos
- **G** plaza
- **H** chilli
- **E** cazuela de ave
- **B** pastel de choclo

A. herbal tea
B. baked corn casserole
C. mushrooms—a word that refers to the slums in Chile because they seem to pop up overnight
D. huge estates
E. hearty chicken, rice and vegetable stew
F. farm workers
G. public square
H. where the land ends; Chile's name
I. Chilean cowboy

Illustrate one of the terms above.

> Illustrations will vary.

Research the Spanish language. Write ten Spanish words and the definition for each one.

1. _____ Answers will vary. _____
2. _____
3. _____
4. _____
5. _____
6. _____
7. _____
8. _____
9. _____
10. _____

© Instructional Fair, Inc.   41   IF8799 South America

Colombia
(kuh-LUHM-bee-uh)

Name _____

Physical Features

1. On the map, draw a star to mark the location of the capital of Colombia. Write the name nearby.
2. Label the countries and bodies of water that border Colombia.
3. Use ^^^ to mark the location of the Andes Mountains on the map.
4. **Cristóbal Colón** is Colombia's highest mountain. It rises **18,947** feet, or **5775** meters, above sea level. Use a small cross (+) to mark its location on the map.
5. Describe the physical features of the three major land regions that make up Colombia.

Coastal Lowlands _____ Descriptions will vary. _____

Andes Mountains _____

Eastern Plains _____

6. Define *llanos* _prairie-like grassland found on eastern plains_
7. The Nevado del Ruiz, located in the Andes Mountains west of Bogotá, is an _active volcano_. Use a red triangle to mark its location on the map.

© Instructional Fair, Inc.   42   IF8799 South America

Colombia

Name _____

History

1. Color the flag of Colombia in its correct colors.
2. The yellow stripe in Colombia's flag represents _the golden new world_. The red stands for _blood shed for independence_ and the blue stands for _the Atlantic Ocean_.
3. _Indian peoples_ inhabited Colombia before the arrival of the Spanish.
4. The Chibcha were an advanced civilization living in the Andes Mountains. They were conquered by the _Spanish_, who named the city of Bogotá after the Cibcha chief _Bacâta_.
5. After the Spanish invasion of Colombia, a new population of people was created by the intermarriage of the Spanish and Indian peoples. A person of mixed Indian and Spanish heritage is known as a _mestizo_. Today, _50_ to _60_ percent of Colombians are of mixed Spanish and Indian descent.
6. Colombia's movement towards independence from the Spanish began in 1780 and 1781, when people were angered by new _taxes_.
7. Spain was finally defeated by Colombia in the year _1819_. The decisive battle, known as _the Battle of Boyacá_ was led by Venezuelan General _Simon Bolivar_.
8. In 1903, Colombia lost _Panama_ when the Colombian Senate refused to allow the United States to build a canal from the Atlantic to the Pacific Ocean. Panama revolted.
9. In 1922, Colombia was paid _$25_ million by the U.S. for the loss of Panama.
10. Colombia is named after explorer _Christopher Columbus_.

Extension: On another paper, describe what happened in Colombia during the period known as *La Violencia* (The Violence).

© Instructional Fair, Inc.   43   IF8799 South America

Colombia

Use with page 18.

Name _____

Puracé National Park

Puracé is a national park in Colombia. The park has a snow-covered, active volcano which is more than 15,000 feet tall. *Páramos*, which are high, bleak Andean plateaus or alpine meadows, are also found in the park. The wet, rainy meadows of the *páramos* are home to many types of animals. The park is a refuge for the pudu, the mountain tapir, the condor, and the spectacled bear. Puracé became a national park in 1961 and covers 320 square miles (830 sq. km).

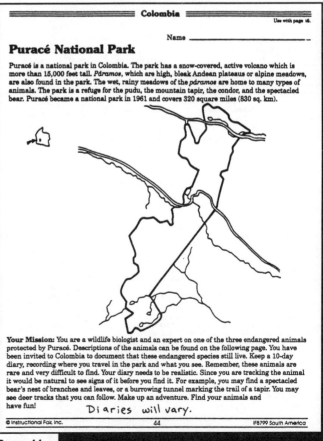

Your Mission: You are a wildlife biologist and an expert on one of the three endangered animals protected by Puracé. Descriptions of the animals can be found on the following page. You have been invited to Colombia to document that these endangered species still live. Keep a 10-day diary, recording where you travel in the park and what you see. Remember, these animals are rare and very difficult to find. Your diary needs to be realistic. Since you are tracking the animal it would be natural to see signs of it before you find it. For example, you may find a spectacled bear's nest of branches and leaves, or a burrowing tunnel marking the trail of a tapir. You may see deer tracks that you can follow. Make up an adventure. Find your animals and have fun!

> Diaries will vary.

© Instructional Fair, Inc.   44   IF8799 South America

Name _____

Puracé National Park
Animal Descriptions

Spectacled Bear

This is the only kind of bear found in South America. Mostly black, with yellow or white patches of fur around its eyes, the spectacled bear prefers to live in cool, high forests, including the *páramo* area of Puracé National Park. This bear makes nests for itself with branches and leaves, but it rarely stays in one place for long and may travel long distances in search of food. It eats fruits, leaves, and roots. The spectacled bear is in danger of becoming extinct because its forest homes are being destroyed and because it has been overhunted. Protected areas like Puracé National Park are the only places these animals are safe from humans.

Mountain Tapir

This animal is similar to a hog or boar in appearance, though it is related to the horse and the rhinoceros. There are two kinds of South American tapirs, lowland and mountain. The mountain tapir is quite rare. Like the lowland tapir, it lives by water. Tapirs love to swim! This animal makes tunnel-like trails through the undergrowth. This makes the animal particularly difficult to see. It is found in elevations of 6,500 to 14,500 feet and lives in heavy plant undergrowth. Tapirs eat twigs and leaves off trees and shrubs, as well as any fruits or vegetables they can find. The mountain tapir has long been hunted for its meat and thick hide. Its forest habitat is quickly disappearing due to extensive logging and agricultural activity.

Pudu

These tiny deer are only about one foot high and are known for their shyness. They have tiny, spiked antlers. Pudu live in the *páramo* as well as forested areas which range from sea level to altitudes of 10,000 feet (3,000 meters). Pudu are found only in South America. These animals do not have a permanent den or nesting site. They roam in herds or alone in search of food. Deer are herbivores: they eat only plants. Their diet consists mostly of grasses, flowers, buds, leaves, and in lean times, bark or twigs. Pudu are the smallest of all deer. Their coat is rough and brown or gray. Amazingly, these deer are considered hunting trophies. Habitat destruction, though, is the biggest threat to their continued existence.

Page 45

Name _____

Birds of Colombia

Read the information below. In the box draw a picture of the bird described. Be sure to pay attention to size, wingspan, markings, and color so your drawing is accurate. You may want to make a rough sketch of the bird as you read and then draw it again neatly on this page.

Pictures will vary.

Sword-Billed Hummingbird

The male sword-billed hummingbird grows to about 5.8 inches tall. It is known for its enormously long bill which is heavy and slightly upturned. The bill is about 4 inches long (almost as long as the bird is tall!) The bird has a bronze head and bronze-green feathers covering the rest of its back. Its throat is brown-black and its underparts are bright green. Its 2-inch-long split tail is bronze green. This bird lives in the Andes mountains in Colombia, as well as in Ecuador, Peru, and Bolivia.

Blue-Crowned Motmot

Motmots are a small family of tropical birds. Motmots live in dark forests, feeding on fruits, insects, and reptiles. The blue-crowned motmot grows from 15 to 17 inches tall. It has a long bill, approximately 3 inches long. The very top of its head and forehead are black, and the sides of the head are a brilliant turquoise that changes to an ultramarine blue on the lower sides and back of the bird's head. The back is grass green with a tinge of light blue on the tips of the wings. It has a black spot bordered by turquoise blue in the middle of its olive green and cinnamon chest. The tail is longer than its body and is green, becoming blue at the very end, tipped with black. This is a vibrantly colored bird with a very, very long tail.

Extension: Write a description of an animal or bird and have a classmate try to draw the animal from what you wrote.

Page 46

Name _____

Smuggling

The Problem

Animals are stolen from South America, smuggled to different parts of the world, and sold to people as pets for a tremendous profit. It is illegal to remove animals from South America without a permit. So much of the continent is densely forested that it is difficult to catch people illegally trapping the animals.

The smugglers are interested only in the profit they can make. They do not care about the laws or the animals. Smugglers have been known to put over 300 birds in one box to illegally ship them out of South America. If only half of the birds live, the smugglers believe that it has been profitable. These people will also try to make animals more attractive to buyers. They have been known to paint green parakeets fantastic colors: red, purples, oranges, and yellows. When the bird molts, the painted feathers drop out, leaving the bird its original green color once again. By this time, however, the crook is far away.

• On another paper, write a paragraph telling why you think that it should or should not be illegal to sell South American animals as pets. Then devise some ways the South American government could fight this problem and write about them.

The Solution?

South American officials are battling the problem of animal-napping and smuggling. When they discover an illegal shipment of animals, they arrest the culprits and return the animals to South America. Captured animals are sent to a center for rehabilitation with the hope that they can be released into the wild.

Even when the officials feel the animal is ready to be released into the wild, they often don't know where the animal originated. To add to this dilemma, there are many subspecies of any one species. This means that a parrot from the rain forest of Brazil is different from the same species of parrot from the forests of Colombia. It is extremely difficult, though, to determine these minute differences. If an animal is released in the wrong area, it could change the face of the population in that area, perhaps endangering the survival of the animals already living there.

• Do you think animals should be rehabilitated and released into the wild? Why or why not? On another paper, explain your views in a paragraph.

Page 47

Name _____

Poetry

Colombians have great regard for writers, especially poets. Writers are so admired that many teachers, lawyers, doctors, and other professional people spend their spare time writing poetry. Colombians boast that more poets than generals have been elected president.

Below are some descriptions of Colombian life. After each, write a *couplet* that will give readers a feeling for what you read.

> A *couplet* is a verse composed of two lines which can, but do not have to, rhyme. One of the keys to writing good verse is to take your time and think about the flow and sound of your words when they are read aloud. It is not unusual for poetry to require more rewriting than descriptive writing.

Colombians enjoy thick stews and soups. One of their favorites is a delicious soup made from tender chicken, potatoes, and corn. The soup is called *ajiaco* (ah hee AH koh). Potatoes are a staple in the diets of many Colombians.

Example: Bubbling, steaming, mouth-watering smells fill my head with memories
           Of fall earth bursting with potatoes, waiting to become ajiaco.

_____ Couplets will vary. _____

Colombia is the only country in South America which borders both the Pacific Ocean and the Caribbean Sea in the Atlantic Ocean. The many rivers and swamps provided early Colombian people with a natural transportation route. Native peoples traveled, migrated, and traded with each other using dug-out canoes. Imagine traveling along a coast in the turquoise blue of the Caribbean Sea and looking towards a dark green, mysterious rain forest teeming with the sounds of life.

_____

Soccer is Colombia's national sport. Two teams with 11 players on each side try to kick or hit a round white and black ball into the other team's goal using any body part except the hands. Soccer was invented in England, but has become the world's most popular sport. More than 140 countries world-wide have soccer teams. Playing this game well requires a lot of athletic skill and ability. Players need to know how to kick, pass, tackle, fake, dribble, and head the ball.

_____

Page 48

Name _____

Picaresque

The *picaresque* is a type of story where the main character is a villainous, nasty, unlikable person. This type of story is not written with one continuous plot, but is written as a series of events or incidents that describe the main character's life. These bits and pieces of life are then put together to create an entire story. The *picaresque* was invented in Spain, but Colombians are famous for this type of writing.

Choose one of the following subjects. Research your choice, thinking carefully about the types of people who would have been involved. Using what you've learned, create a main character who is a "bad guy." Write about one event that happened during the life of your main character.

slavery	Spanish invasion	La Violencia
piracy	conquistadors	bull fighting

Stories will vary.

_____

Extension: As a class, create a "bad guy." Then, write a class *picaresque* featuring your "bad guy" as the main character. Each day, the story is given to a different student who reads what has been written so far and adds one written event in the main character's life to that. When everyone has had a turn to add to the class book, the *picaresque* is complete.

Page 49

Name _____

El Dorado

The Chibchas people lived in Colombia long before the Spanish invaded. They believed that a meteor fell to earth creating a huge hole that became Guatavita Lake. This lake was special to the Chibchas, so they held ceremonies at its shore, including initiation ceremonies for new Chibchas leaders. A new chief would cover his body in a sticky, glue-like substance. Then gold dust would be sprinkled all over the glue, making the chief into a living golden statue. The golden leader was rowed on a raft to the middle of the lake where he would dive in. The gold would wash off in the water. This was the new chief's way of offering gold to the lake. At the same time, people in the raft and on shore would throw gold and jewels into the lake as a further offering.

This Chibchas ceremony was probably the basis for the fanatical search for El Dorado, the fictitious kingdom of fabulous riches and wealth. The Spanish pursued this dream with a vengeance. The legend of El Dorado was the cause of much death and strife for the native people of Colombia.

Maps will vary.

1. Create a Colombian treasure map. This map may include only a portion of the country or may cover all of Colombia. Draw natural features and cities as landmarks on the map.

2. Write a letter that goes with the map, giving hints and clues to where a treasure hunter should start as well as warnings against dangers. Use directions, landmarks, or facts to direct treasure hunters on your map.

3. Trade your map and treasure hunt description with another student. Each of you should try to locate El Dorado.

Note: There are no rules. Make the maps and descriptions fair, but fun. There should be a final location for El Dorado, but you may make the hunt as mysterious and difficult as you would like. For instance, you might use a riddle, or a treasure hunter might have to collect clues from each landmark on the map to discover where El Dorado is. Use your imagination. Happy hunting!

Page 50

Name _____

Map Activity

Make a pictorial map of Colombia. Draw and color a variety of pictures on the map that relate to the country of Colombia. These pictures might include animals, plants, crops, places of interest, famous people, etc. Include at least 12 different topics. Include a key on the bottom of your map that explains what your pictures represent.

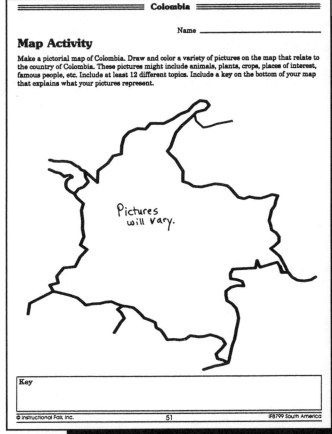

Pictures will vary.

Key

Page 51

(EHK-wuh-dawr)

Name _____

Physical Features

1. On the map, draw a star to mark the location of the capital of Ecuador. Write the name nearby.

2. Write the names of the two countries and body of water that border Ecuador on the map.

3. Draw the equator on the map.

4. Locate the Andes Mountains. Label them on the map using the symbol ∧∧∧.

5. Ecuador was named for <u>the equator which cuts across it</u>. Ecuador is the Spanish word for <u>equator</u>.

(Map shows: Pacific Ocean, Colombia, Galapagos Islands, Quito, Equator, Guayaquil, Peru)

6. On the map, draw a dot to mark the location of Ecuador's largest city. Write the name nearby.

7. The Galapagos Islands, approximately 600 miles (970 kilometers) off the coast, belong to Ecuador. These islands are known for their unusual <u>animals</u> and <u>plants</u>.

8. Ecuador is one of the <u>smallest</u> (smallest, largest) countries of South America.

9. The country contains large <u>petroleum</u> deposits.

10. The <u>valleys</u> and <u>plateaus</u> of the Andes Mountains are where about half of the people of Ecuador live.

11. A big <u>jungle</u> is located east of the Andes Mountains. Not many people live there.

12. Ecuador has three land regions. Write a brief description of each.

The Coastal Lowland <u>Descriptions will vary.</u>

The Andes Highland _____

The Eastern Lowland _____

Page 52

History

Name _____

1. Color Ecuador's flag with its correct colors.
2. Communication in Ecuador is very primitive. Write two facts that support this statement.
   Answers might include that there are few radios, televisions, or telephones.
3. Write a fact that you think is important about each of the following periods in Ecuador's history.

Indian Period: _Facts will vary._

Spanish Rule: _____

Independence: _____

During the 1900s: _____

In the box below, illustrate one of the facts you just listed.

Page 53

Culture and People

Name _____

1. What do people do at the market shown in the picture? _Answers will vary — might include these:_
   Buy and sell food and handicrafts, meeting friends, listen to music, and so on.
2. Most Ecuadorians speak what language?
   Spanish
3. Why are some children unable to attend school in the rural areas of Ecuador?
   Answers will vary. There are not many schools in rural areas; some children may have to work; and so on.
4. Many Ecuadorians cannot read or write. How do you think this affects their lives?
   Answers will vary.
5. About 10 percent of Ecuador's population, mostly people of European ancestry, make up the _wealthiest_ (wealthiest, poorest) group in the country.
6. Indians and *mestizos*, who are people of mixed _Indian_ and _White_ ancestry, each make up about 40 percent of Ecuador's population.
7. _Blacks_, whose ancestors were slaves, form 10 percent of the population.
8. Describe what it is like to live in an Indian Village in Ecuador.
   Descriptions will vary.

Page 54

Cities in Ecuador

Name _____

Ambato	Esmeraldas	Machala	Portoviejo
Cuenca	Guayaquil	Manta	Quito

Find the location of each of these cities on a map of Ecuador.

Choose one of the above cities in Ecuador to study. Write a description of this city to share with others.

Name of city: _Answers will vary._

I chose this city to study because _____

The population of this city was _____ in the year _____

Write a description of the city.

Page 55

Galapagos Islands

Name _____

1. The Galapagos Islands were once known as the
   Enchanted Isles.
2. The Galapagos Islands are owned by _Ecuador_.
3. Name the five largest Galapagos Islands.
   Isabela,
   Santa Cruz,
   San Cristóbal
   Fernandina
   San Salvador
   Label these five islands on the map.
4. Label the ocean which surrounds the islands on the map.
5. The Galapagos Islands span about _3,000_ square miles (_7,800_ square kilometers).
6. Most of the islands are _volcano_ peaks.
7. The islands are also called the _Archipiélago_ de _Colón_.
8. Research the Galapagos Islands. Record here some facts you find interesting about these islands.
   Facts will vary.

Source: _____ Page(s): _____

Page 56

Name _____

Galapagos Islands Art

Read as much as possible about the Galapagos Islands, which are owned by Ecuador. Draw, color, and label pictures relating to these islands in the frame below. Cut out the frame and display the picture in your classroom.

G
A
L
A
P
A
G
O
S

I
S
L
A
N
D
S

Art
will
vary.

© Instructional Fair, Inc.　　　57　　　IF8799 South America

Page 57

Name _____

Map Activity

Make a pictorial map of Ecuador. Draw and color a variety of pictures on the map that relate to the country of Ecuador. These pictures might include animals, plants, crops, places of interest, famous people, etc. Include at least 12 different topics. Include a key on the bottom of your map that explains what your pictures represent.

Pictures
will
vary.

Key

© Instructional Fair, Inc.　　　58　　　IF8799 South America

Page 58

Name _____

Physical Features

1. On the map, draw a star to mark the location of the capital of Guyana. Write the name nearby.
2. On the map, label the three countries and the body of water that border Guyana.
3. Give a description of each of the three main land regions found in Guyana.

The coastal plain _Descriptions_
will vary.
_____
_____

The inland forest _____
_____

The highland _____

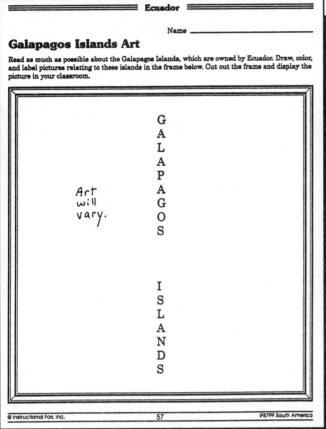

Venezuela
North Atlantic Ocean
Georgetown
Suriname
Brazil

4. The four main rivers of Guyana flow north into the Atlantic Ocean. Name these rivers.

   Essequibo　　　_Berbice_
   Demerara　　　_Courantyne_

5. There are many spectacular waterfalls located throughout Guyana. Tell where each of the following waterfalls is located and give the height or drop distance for each one.

   King George VI Falls _Utashi River - 1600 foot drop_
   Great Falls _Mazaruni River - 840 foot drop_
   Kaieteur Falls _Potaro River - 741 foot drop_

© Instructional Fair, Inc.　　　59　　　IF8799 South America

Page 59

Name _____

General Information

plantains
coffee
coconuts
sugar cane
cocoa
rice
citrus fruits

1. In the circle above, write the names of seven important crops grown in Guyana.
2. The two largest ethnic groups found in Guyana are the _East Indians_ and the _Blacks_.
3. The official language of the people of Guyana is _English_, but many of the people speak a broken form of English called _Creolese_.
4. Guyana's East Indians speak _Hindi_ and _Urdu_.
5. The East Indians of Guyana live in rural areas and work on _sugar plantations_ or small farms where they grow _rice_ and _vegetables_. Their ancestors came from _India_. Some East Indians have moved to cities and towns and work as _doctors_, _lawyers_, and _merchants_.
6. The blacks of Guyana live in the cities and towns and many work as skilled workers in the _sugar grinding_ mills and _bauxite_ mines. Others are _teachers_, _police officers_, and _government workers_.
7. The most important kind of tree that grows in Guyana is the _greenheart_, because it is used for making _wharves_, where boats can dock to load and unload cargo.
8. Some Amerindians live in remote forest areas. Some make their living by _hunting_ and others by _farming_ or _cutting timber_.

© Instructional Fair, Inc.　　　60　　　IF8799 South America

Page 60

Guyana

Name _____

History

1. Color the flag of Guyana with its correct colors. Give the meaning of the colors and symbols on the flag.

green= agriculture and forests; red triangle= dedication in building Nation; yellow arrowhead= minerals; white outline = water resources

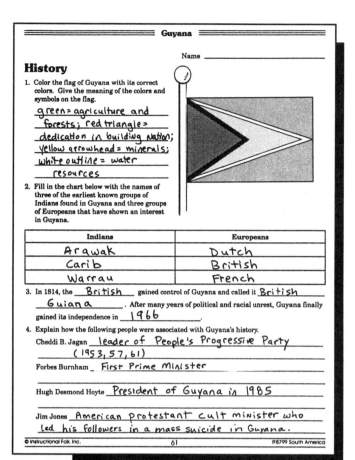

2. Fill in the chart below with the names of three of the earliest known groups of Indians found in Guyana and three groups of Europeans that have shown an interest in Guyana.

Indians	Europeans
Arawak	Dutch
Carib	British
Warrau	French

3. In 1814, the __British__ gained control of Guyana and called it __British Guiana__. After many years of political and racial unrest, Guyana finally gained its independence in __1966__.

4. Explain how the following people were associated with Guyana's history.

Cheddi B. Jagan __leader of People's Progressive Party (1953, 57, 61)__

Forbes Burnham __First Prime Minister__

Hugh Desmond Hoyte __President of Guyana in 1985__

Jim Jones __American protestant cult minister who led his followers in a mass suicide in Guyana.__

© Instructional Fair, Inc.   61   IF8799 South America

Guyana

Name _____

Map Activity

Make a pictorial map of Guyana. Draw and color a variety of different pictures on the map that relate to the country of Guyana. These pictures might include animals, plants, crops, places of interest, famous people, etc. Include at least 12 different topics. Include a key on the bottom of your map that explains what your pictures represent.

Pictures will vary

Key

© Instructional Fair, Inc.   62   IF8799 South America

Paraguay
(PAIR-uh-GWAY)

Name _____

Physical Features

1. On the map, draw a star to mark the location of the capital of Paraguay. Write the name nearby.

2. On the map, label the countries that border Paraguay.

3. Paraguay is a landlocked country. Landlocked means

enclosed by land; not bordered by a body of water

4. The __Pilcomayo__ River creates the border between Paraguay and Argentina. Mark this river in blue on the map and label it.

5. The __Paraguay__ River divides the country into two major regions. Use green to draw and label this river on the map.

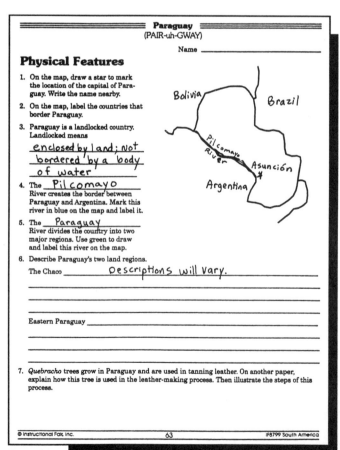

6. Describe Paraguay's two land regions.

The Chaco __Descriptions will vary.__

Eastern Paraguay _____

7. *Quebracho* trees grow in Paraguay and are used in tanning leather. On another paper, explain how this tree is used in the leather-making process. Then illustrate the steps of this process.

© Instructional Fair, Inc.   63   IF8799 South America

Paraguay

Name _____

History

1. Color the flag of Paraguay with its correct colors.

2. Why is the design of Paraguay's flag considered unusual?

It is the only National flag with different designs on both sides

3. __Guaraní Indians__ were the first people to live in Paraguay.

4. __Spanish__ and __Portuguese__ explorers were the first whites to arrive in Paraguay. They were searching for __a route to Peru and treasures there of silver and gold__.

5. Missionaries of the __Jesuit__ order came to Paraguay in 1588 to convert the Guaraní to __Roman Catholicism__. They formed mission settlements called __reducciones or reductions__ where the Indians lived and worked.

6. Today, both __Spanish__ and __Guaraní__ are languages spoken in Paraguay.

7. __Asunción__ was the first Spanish settlement in Paraguay and is now the country's capital.

8. In the year __1811__, Paraguayans overthrew the Spanish governor and declared their independence.

9. For a time, rival political groups struggled for power. Paraguay had more than __30__ presidents from 1870 to 1932.

10. Why did Paraguay go to war with Bolivia? What was the result of that war?

They went to war over a land dispute. As a result, Paraguay gained new territory in Chaco.

© Instructional Fair, Inc.   64   IF8799 South America

Jesuit Reductions

Purpose for reading: read the following description as a class. Define *Jesuit*, *slavery*, *missionary*, and *colonist*.

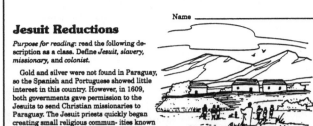

Gold and silver were not found in Paraguay, so the Spanish and Portuguese showed little interest in this country. However, in 1609, both governments gave permission to the Jesuits to send Christian missionaries to Paraguay. The Jesuit priests quickly began creating small religious commun- ities known as *reductions*, or *reducciones*.

Reduction means the "gathering together" of people. In this case, the Guaraní Indians were "gathered" by the priests. The Jesuit priests brought the Indians into self-sufficient communities to teach them Christianity, to bring European culture to them, and to protect them from other European colonists and explorers. Slave trading was common. South American native people were often captured by Spanish and Portuguese colonists and sold into slavery, even though it was illegal.

Each reduction consisted of approximately 4,000 Guaraní with two or three Jesuit leaders. Paraguay had 30 such reductions. Under the Jesuits, the Guaraní learned advanced agricultural techniques and grew crops of sugarcane, cotton, rice, tobacco, and wheat. The Guaraní were taught the Christian religion as well as the skills of carpentry, masonry, blacksmithing, and woodworking. The Guaraní also learned about painting, sculpture, calligraphy, and music from the priests.

In 1767, the Jesuits were expelled from Paraguay. The reductions fell into ruin, leaving over 100,000 Indians to fend for themselves. Some Indians returned to the depths of the Chaco and some worked on the estates of Spanish colonists. Others fled to the cities, and others were caught and enslaved or died.

- Divide the class into two factions. Each group should prepare for a debate. Three people should be chosen from each group to represent that group in a debate.

- One side will defend the Jesuits and the Reduction way of life. This group will want to focus on the protection provided by the Jesuits, the skills taught, and the chaos that reigned when the Jesuits were expelled.

- The other group will be opposed to the Jesuits and their gathering of the Guaraní Indians. This group will want to concentrate on the idea of slavery and the appropriateness of imposing a different culture and religion on a group of people.

Extension: Students write an opinion paper following the debate answering this question: Did Reductions provide a good or bad way of life for the Guaraní? Why?

Page 65

Ñandutí Lace

Ñandutí describes a style of intricate lace unique to Paraguay. It was introduced to Paraguay by the Jesuit priests. Very large lace hangings have been created and each ñandutí pattern has its own name. In Paraguay, it is customary to tie a band of ñandutí lace around a black cross in remembrance of a deceased friend.

Nanduti Lace   Italian Lace   Spider web

Answers will vary.

Compare and Contrast

In the columns below, use adjectives to compare the two types of lace and the spider web. An adjective may be used for all three, only two, or only one.

Use the three columns below to list the different shapes you find in the drawings above.

Extension: Find a piece of lace. On another piece of paper, use complete sentences to answer the following questions: Where did you find the lace? Is the lace you found similar to those drawn above? How could this lace be used?

Page 66

Itaipú Dam

The Itaipú Dam on the Paraná River on the Paraguay-Brazil border is one of the largest hydroelectric power projects in the world. *Hydro* is the Greek word for water. A hydro-electric dam generates electricity by using water power and is built across riverbeds. The water is trapped on the up- stream side of the dam, forming a reservoir on one side. Power is generated by water forced into huge wheels located under the dam. These huge wheels are called turbines. The turbines are turned by the enormous force of the water and drive another machine called a generator which produces electricity. The water acts as a powerful force because it is under tremendous pressure.

Background for Experiment:
Deep water is under greater pressure than shallow water. That is one reason why underwater divers have to be careful about rising too quickly to the surface of the water after diving deeply. Their bodies have to adjust to the greater pressure as they dive and must reverse this process as they rise to the surface.

Experiment:
Prove this to yourself. Take five plastic soda bottles. With a permanent ink marker, mark a line at 2" increments up the side of each bottle. Fill the bottles with water. Take the bottles outside and set the first one on the sidewalk. Poke a hole at the highest mark on the bottle. Watch carefully. Use chalk to mark the furthest point the water spouted when the hole was poked. Repeat this by poking holes on each of the lower marks on the remaining bottles. Make sure you put the bottles in the same spot each time before making your hole. Also, make holes approximately the same size. This will insure that your results are accurate.

Answers will vary.

What did you learn about water pressure? _____

Page 67

More About Itaipú Dam

Concrete dams are the strongest of all dams. Still, for a concrete dam to be strong enough to hold an enormous amount of water in a reservoir, the base of the dam has to be built very thickly. On concrete dams, the base's width is roughly ¾ of the height of the dam. For example, if the height of a dam was 80 feet, then the base would be 60 feet thick. Show your math when figuring out the questions below.

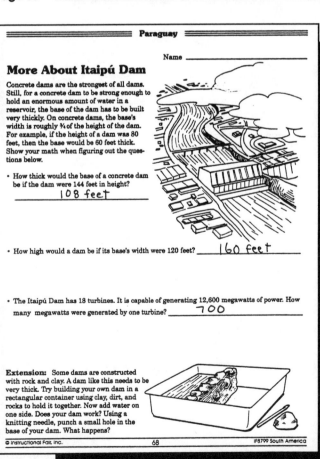

- How thick would the base of a concrete dam be if the dam were 144 feet in height?

  108 feet

- How high would a dam be if its base's width were 120 feet? *160 feet*

- The Itaipú Dam has 18 turbines. It is capable of generating 12,600 megawatts of power. How many megawatts were generated by one turbine? *700*

Extension: Some dams are constructed with rock and clay. A dam like this needs to be very thick. Try building your own dam in a rectangular container using clay, dirt, and rocks to hold it together. Now add water on one side. Does your dam work? Using a knitting needle, punch a small hole in the base of your dam. What happens?

Page 68

The Wars

Name _____

Read about the following two wars and tell how each affected Paraguay. Be sure to include who the wars were fought against, how long they lasted, and what the results of the wars were. Use complete sentences in your narratives.

Answers will vary. Answers will include these facts:

War of the Triple Alliance

Against Brazil and Argentina and Uruguay
1856-1870
Paraguay lost a large portion of its population and was left in ruins.

Chaco War

Against Bolivia
1932 to 1938
Paraguay lost more population, but signed a treaty in 1935. In 1938, a final settlement awarded Paraguay with a new territory in the Chaco region.

Page 69

Map Activity

Name _____

Make a pictorial map of Paraguay. Draw and color a variety of pictures on the map that relate to the country of Paraguay. These pictures might include animals, plants, crops, places of interest, famous people, etc. Include at least 12 different topics. Include a key on the bottom of your map that explains what your pictures represent.

Pictures will vary.

Key _____

Page 70

Physical Features

Name _____

1. On the map, draw a star to mark the location of the capital of Peru. Write the name nearby.
2. Draw and label the mountains in Peru on the map.
3. On the map, label the body of water and the five countries that border Peru.
4. Peru is the third largest country in South America. List the South American countries that are larger than Peru.
   Brazil
   Argentina
5. What is the Peru Current? It is an unusually cold ocean current that makes the Peruvian coast cooler than most tropical coasts.
6. There are three main land regions in Peru. Write a brief description of each of them.
   Coast: Descriptions will vary.

   Highlands: _____

   The Selva: _____

   Label and shade in these land regions on the map.
7. Peru's largest lake is Lake Titicaca . Part of this lake lies in Bolivia .
8. South America's longest river, the Amazon River, flows through Peru.
9. Peru does lie entirely within the tropics.
   (does, does not)

Page 71

History

Name _____

1. Color the flag of Peru with its correct colors.
2. Probably the first people to live in Peru were Indians who came from the continent of North America . The names of early tribes were
   Chavin ,
   Mochica ,
   Tiahuanaco , and
   Chimu .
3. What food first grew wild in the highlands of Peru and then was cultivated in Peru as well as in many other countries? potatoes
4. What year did Peru's first constitution go into effect? 1827
5. Peru's first president was General José de la Mar .
6. Peru lost its valuable nitrate deposits as a result of the War of the Pacific.
7. Name two other important dates and events that took place in Peru.
   Date: _____ Event: Answers will vary.

   Source: _____ Page(s): _____

   Date: _____ Event: _____

   Source: _____ Page(s): _____
8. Write a question that you might ask others relating to the history of Peru.
   Question: _____
   Answer: _____
   Source: _____ Page(s) _____

Page 72

Culture and People

Name _____

1. Write a paragraph about the ruins of Machu Picchu, shown in the picture above.
   Paragraph might include that it was a walled Incan city which stood near the mountain Cusco.

2. The two official languages of Peru are __Spanish__ and __Quechua__.

3. What recreational activities do the Peruvians enjoy? Underline the two that you would enjoy most if you lived in Peru.
   music, dancing, soccer, basketball, bullfighting, festivals, and games

4. Who was Peruvian Ricardo Palma?
   The first great Peruvian writer. He wrote about colonial life in Peru.

5. The Indians of Peru make unique arts and crafts. Learn about some of their art works. Draw two or more examples of their work in the box below:

Page 73

Cities of Peru

Name _____

Arequipa, Calloa, Cusco, and Lima are all cities of Peru. Research two cities of Peru. Write three facts about each of them.

Answers will vary.

1. City: _____
   Fact: _____
   Fact: _____
   Fact: _____
   Source: _____ Page(s): _____

2. City: _____
   Fact: _____
   Fact: _____
   Fact: _____
   Source: _____ Page(s): _____

Which one of these cities would you prefer to live in if you moved to Peru? Why?
_____
_____
_____
_____

Page 74

Coat of Arms

Name _____

Find a picture of the Peruvian coat of arms. Draw and color it, including the three symbols that belong on the shield.

What do the three symbols represent?
The symbols represent Peru's abundant animal, plant, and mineral resources.

Source: _____ Page(s): _____

Page 75

Map Activity

Name _____

Make a pictorial map of Peru. Draw and color a variety of pictures on the map that relate to the country of Peru. These pictures might include animals, plants, crops, places of interest, famous people, etc. Include at least 12 different topics. Include a key on the bottom of your map that explains what your pictures represent.

Pictures will vary.

Key

Page 76

Peru

Name ______

Homes in Peru

Describe different types of homes found in Peru. Then draw and label two of them in the frames below.

Descriptions will vary.

© Instructional Fair, Inc. 77 IF8799 South America

Page 77

Peru

Name ______

Fishing in Peru

Peru is a leading fishing country. The main fish that the Peruvians catch in the ocean are anchovies, sardines, and tuna. Research these fish. Note their shapes and colors. Draw these fish as part of an ocean scene below.

Pictures will vary.

Source: ______ Page(s): ______
Source: ______ Page(s): ______
Source: ______ Page(s): ______

© Instructional Fair, Inc. 78 IF8799 South America

Page 78

Suriname
(sur-ree-NAHM-uh **or** SOOR-uh-NAHM)

Name ______

Physical Features

1. On the map, draw a star to mark the location of the capital of Suriname. Write the name nearby.
2. Label the three countries and the body of water that border Suriname.
3. Describe the three land regions found in Suriname.

narrow coastal area Descriptions will vary.

mountainous rain forests ______

savanna ______

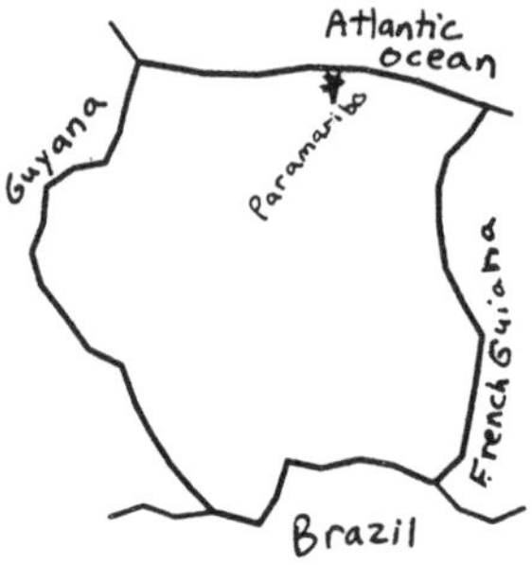

Atlantic Ocean
Paramaribo
Guyana
French Guiana
Brazil

4. Most of the people live in the flat, coastal area of Suriname.
5. Suriname is the smallest (smallest, largest) independent country in South America in both area and population.
6. Name the two types of businesses on which the economy of Suriname is based.
mining metal processing
7. Suriname's rivers provide the country's main means of transportation.
8. The highest elevation found in Suriname is Mount Juliana Top.

© Instructional Fair, Inc. 79 IF8799 South America

Page 79

Suriname

Name ______

General Information

1. List the seven different ethnic groups found throughout Suriname in descending order of population on the ladder.
   1. Hindustanis
   2. Creoles
   3. Indonesians
   4. Maroons
   5. American Indians
   6. Chinese
   7. Europeans
2. Suriname's official language is Dutch, but most Surinamese speak Sranan Tongo. This language combines elements of English, Dutch, and several African languages
3. Give a general description of the lifestyles of the following groups of people found throughout Suriname:
Hindustanis Descriptions will vary.
Creoles ______
Indonesians ______
Maroons ______
4. Nearly half (half, one-quarter) of Suriname's population lives in Paramaribo.
5. Name Suriname's three major export products.
bauxite aluminum rice
6. Rice is grown on three-fourths of Suriname's farmland.
7. Some other crops grown in Suriname are bananas, sugar, coconuts, etc.
8. The forests of Suriname produce a large quantity of hardwoods that are used for logs and plywood.
9. The basic unit of money in Suriname is the guilder.

© Instructional Fair, Inc. 80 IF8799 South America

Page 80

History

Name _____

1. Color the flag of Suriname with its correct colors.

2. Name the European countries that owned Suriname during its years of growth and development.

   <u>Netherlands</u>
   <u>Britain</u>

3. What did the Dutch give the British in exchange for Suriname in 1667?

   <u>What became the state</u>
   <u>of New York</u>

4. Years of conflict between the different ethnic groups in Suriname delayed its independence until <u>1975</u>.

5. Describe Suriname's National Assembly.

   <u>Descriptions will vary but may include that there</u>
   <u>are 51 members who hold five-year terms of</u>
   <u>office; has president and vice-president elected by</u>
   <u>members.</u>

6. Give another accepted spelling for Suriname. <u>Surinam</u>

7. Before Suriname became an independent country it was known as

   <u>Dutch Guiana</u>.

8. Before Suriname gained independence, thousands of its people <u>emigrated</u> to the Netherlands. What was the result of this? <u>Shortage of skilled</u> <u>labor and little economic development</u>

9. Slavery was outlawed in Suriname in <u>1863</u>.

Page 81

City Activity

Name _____

Research the city of Paramaribo. Write three questions you might ask others relating to this city.

City: **Paramaribo**   Answers will vary.

1. Question: _____
   Answer: _____
   Source(s): _____ Page(s): _____

2. Question: _____
   Answer: _____
   Source(s): _____ Page(s): _____

3. Question: _____
   Answer: _____
   Source(s): _____ Page(s): _____

Draw a picture or map of a typical neighborhood in Paramaribo. Include people, buildings, streets, a river, and a park. Label each item according to its function in the neighborhood. Then, on another paper, write a short story about life in this neighborhood.

Page 82

Map Activity

Name _____

Label each of the following on the map.

Rivers:
Kabalebo   Courantyne
Nickerie   Maroni
Coppename   Litani
Saramacca   Lawa
Suriname   Tapanahoni

Lake:
Blommestein Lake

Highest point:
Juliana Top

Draw in these mountain ranges using this symbol ∧∧∧. Label the mountain ranges:
Käyser   Eilerts De Haan
Oranje   Wilhelmina

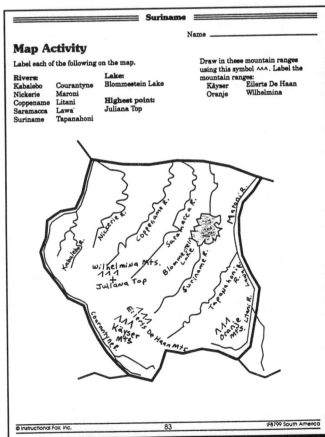

Page 83

Keeping Count of Things in Suriname

Name _____

Fill in the blanks with the correct number.

1. <u>80%</u> The percent of Suriname's land that is covered with mountainous rain forests

2. <u>63,037</u> The area of Suriname in square miles

3. <u>4,200</u> The elevation in feet of Mt. Juliana Top

4. <u>65</u> The percent of the people between ages 15 and 59 who can read

5. <u>75</u> The percentage of exports accounted for by raw bauxite and aluminum

6. <u>800</u> The miles of roads

7. <u>76"</u> The average annual rainfall in west Suriname

8. <u>95"</u> The average annual rainfall in the Paramaribo area

9. <u>81°</u> The average annual temperature

10. <u>463,000</u> The estimated population

Take a count of the following things that pertain to where you live.

1. Your city/town's population: _____   Answers will vary.

2. The total area of your state or province in square miles: _____

3. The average temperature: winter _____ spring _____
   summer _____ fall _____

4. The elevation of the highest point in your state or province: _____

5. The elevation of the lowest point in your state or province: _____

Page 84

Physical Features

1. On the map, draw a star to mark the location of the capital of Uruguay. Write the name nearby.

2. Label the countries and the body of water that border Uruguay.

3. The __Uruguay__ River forms a boundary between Uruguay and Argentina. Using blue, mark and label this river on the map.

4. Uruguay has an area of __68,500__ square miles. The interior lowlands make up about four-fifths of Uruguay's land area. Use the space below to figure about how many square miles are taken up by the lowlands.

   About __54,800__ square miles

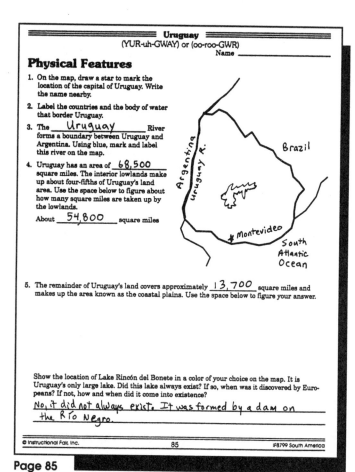

5. The remainder of Uruguay's land covers approximately __13,700__ square miles and makes up the area known as the coastal plains. Use the space below to figure your answer.

Show the location of Lake Rincón del Bonete in a color of your choice on the map. It is Uruguay's only large lake. Did this lake always exist? If so, when was it discovered by Europeans? If not, how and when did it come into existence?

No, it did not always exist. It was formed by a dam on the Río Negro.

History

1. Color the flag of Uruguay with its correct colors.

2. Match each of the following flag and coat of arms symbols with what they represent by drawing a line from each symbol to its meaning.

Symbol	Meaning
Stripes	Liberty and plenty
Scales	Strength
Horse and ox	Justice and equality
Hill of Montevideo	Uruguay's independence
Sun	The way the country was originally divided

3. Read about Uruguay's history. Place the correct date next to each event listed below.

   A. Charrúa Indians, largest group in Uruguay __pre-1516__
   B. *Nova Colonia do Sacramento* established __1680__
   C. Spaniards settle most of Uruguay __1770s__
   D. Spanish colonists establish Montevideo __1726__
   E. Portuguese annex Uruguay to Brazil __1820__
   F. Juan Díaz de Solís lands in Uruguay __1516__
   G. Uruguay adopts its first constitution __1830__
   H. José Batlle y Ordóñez elected President __1903__

4. Place each letter from question #3 at the correct point on the time line. The first one has been done for you.

   ```
   A F              B  D   C   E G      H
   1500  1550  1600  1650  1700  1750  1800  1850  1900
   ```

5. In what year did Uruguay become a charter member of the United Nations? __1945__

6. During the early 1980s, thousands of Uruguayans took part in __antigovernment__ protests. Negotiations between leaders of military and political parties led to __democratic__ elections in 1984 and the formation of a __civilian__ government rather than a __military__ one.

Uruguayan Leader

One man was particularly influential in making Uruguay of the early 1900s a model of democracy: José Batlle. Read about Batlle. Write notes about Batlle in the spaces below.

My notes about Batlle: Answers will vary.

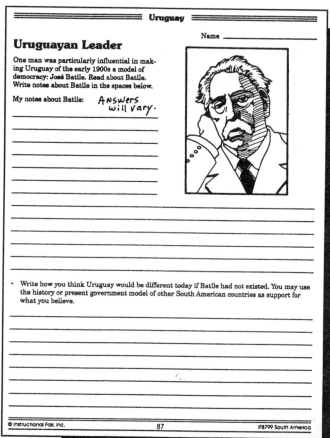

- Write how you think Uruguay would be different today if Batlle had not existed. You may use the history or present government model of other South American countries as support for what you believe.

Montevideo

It is said that all roads in Uruguay lead to Montevideo, its largest city. Montevideo houses 40% of Uruguay's population. Montevideo's historic district, called the "Old Town," has many buildings from the 18th and 19th century. Montevideo is a busy, attractive port city.

Here is a partial map of Montevideo. Below it are various attractions with descriptions of where they can be found in the city. Place the correct corresponding number in each box on the map to show the location of the attraction.

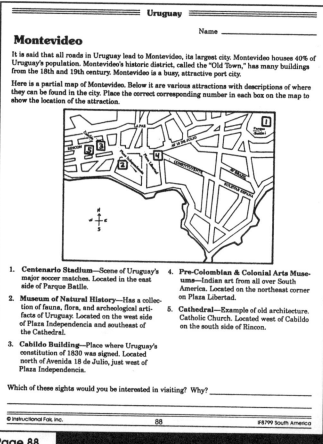

1. **Centenario Stadium**—Scene of Uruguay's major soccer matches. Located in the east side of Parque Batlle.

2. **Museum of Natural History**—Has a collection of fauna, flora, and archeological artifacts of Uruguay. Located on the west side of Plaza Independencia and southeast of the Cathedral.

3. **Cabildo Building**—Place where Uruguay's constitution of 1830 was signed. Located north of Avenida 18 de Julio, just west of Plaza Independencia.

4. **Pre-Colombian & Colonial Arts Museums**—Indian art from all over South America. Located on the northeast corner on Plaza Libertad.

5. **Cathedral**—Example of old architecture. Catholic Church. Located west of Cabildo on the south side of Rincon.

Which of these sights would you be interested in visiting? Why? _____

The Gaucho

Name _____

The gaucho is the Uruguayan version of the American cowboy. During the mid 18th to the mid 19th century, gauchos followed cattle which grazed on Uruguay's rich grasslands. These wanderers followed the herds, bringing them in for sale, living on the range, and eating cattle to survive.

The gaucho has been romanticized in South American literature. For example, in 1872 José Hernández, an Argentinian, wrote the epic poem, "El gaucho Martín Fierro" which describes a gaucho and his life. The poem is widely read and greatly loved in Uruguay.

Read as much as you can find on the gaucho. Choose one of the following assignments.

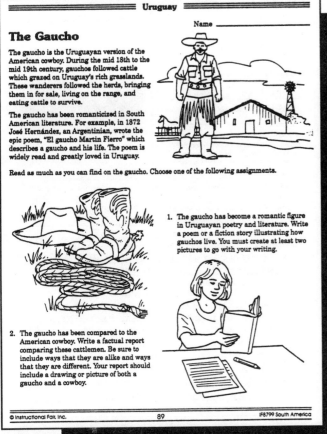

1. The gaucho has become a romantic figure in Uruguayan poetry and literature. Write a poem or a fiction story illustrating how gauchos live. You must create at least two pictures to go with your writing.

2. The gaucho has been compared to the American cowboy. Write a factual report comparing these cattlemen. Be sure to include ways that they are alike and ways that they are different. Your report should include a drawing or picture of both a gaucho and a cowboy.

© Instructional Fair, Inc.   89   IF8799 South America

Page 89

The Economy

Name _____

By South American standards, Uruguay is a wealthy country. Its small population and low population growth have helped its people maintain a fairly high standard of living. Agriculture is one of Uruguay's major economic activities, especially sheep and cattle raising. In fact, 80% of the country's land is used for cattle and sheep estancias. Large amounts of meat are exported to Europe and Brazil.

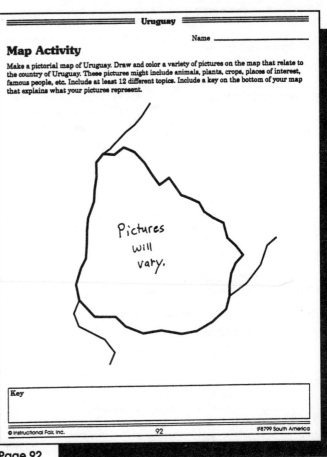

• The world price for beef is important to Uruguay's economy. Read about Uruguay's economy. Write notes about it here. Discuss as a class, how this economy differs from or is similar to that of your own country.

Notes will vary.

_____
_____
_____
_____
_____

• Now do this research project. You have $250,000 to invest in Uruguayan beef. Use the world price chart for beef in a current newspaper paper. How many pounds of beef can you purchase with your money? Answers will vary.

Using the chart on page 91, keep track of world beef prices to determine if you are making or losing money. This financial activity should take at least three weeks. Think about how the farmers of Uruguay are profiting.

On the last day, sell your beef and convert the American dollars into Uruguayan money using an exchange chart in a current newspaper.

© Instructional Fair, Inc.   90   IF8799 South America

Page 90

The Economy (Cont.)

Name _____

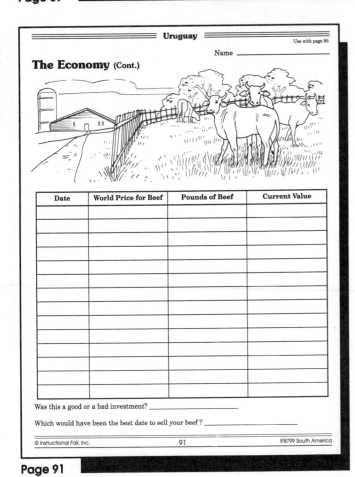

Date	World Price for Beef	Pounds of Beef	Current Value

Was this a good or a bad investment? _____

Which would have been the best date to sell your beef? _____

© Instructional Fair, Inc.   91   IF8799 South America

Page 91

Map Activity

Name _____

Make a pictorial map of Uruguay. Draw and color a variety of pictures on the map that relate to the country of Uruguay. These pictures might include animals, plants, crops, places of interest, famous people, etc. Include at least 12 different topics. Include a key on the bottom of your map that explains what your pictures represent.

Pictures will vary.

Key

© Instructional Fair, Inc.   92   IF8799 South America

Page 92

Physical Features

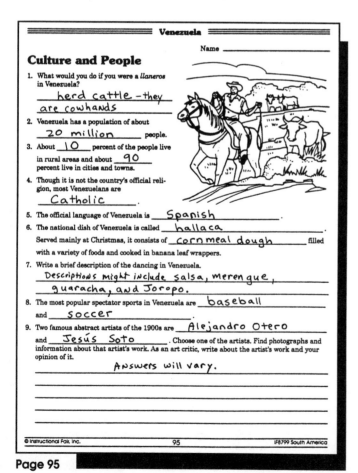

Caribbean Sea
Maracaibo Basin
Andean Highlands
Caracas
Lake Maracaibo
Llanos
Colombia
Guiana Highlands
Guyana
Brazil

1. On the map, draw a star to mark the location of the capital of Venezuela. Write the name nearby.
2. Label the countries and bodies of water that border Venezuela.
3. Draw the boundaries of the four major land regions of Venezuela on the map. Label these regions. Describe each region below.

The Maracaibo Basin _____Descriptions will vary._____

The Andean Highlands _____

The Llanos _____

The Guiana Highlands _____

4. Draw and label Lake Maracaibo on the above map. This is the largest lake in South America and covers __5,217__ square miles, or __13,512__ square kilometers.

History

1. Color the flag of Venezuela with its correct colors.
2. What caused Venezuela to become one of the wealthiest and most rapidly changing countries in South America?

   __It has a large petroleum production.__

3. Indian tribes lived in what is now called Venezuela before settlers from Europe arrived. The chief tribes were from two groups, the __Carib Indians__ and the __Arawak__. Both groups made their livings by __farming__, hunting, fishing, and gathering wild plants.
4. Venezuela was the first Spanish colony in South America to proclaim its independence. Venezuela declared itself independent on __July 5, 1811__. Venezuela was recognized as independent in the year __1821__.
5. After achieving independence, Venezuela had many years of unrest due to...

   __a series of dictators who ruled the country until the mid 1900s__

6. Two dictatorial *caudillos* (leaders) had great influence on Venezuela. Briefly describe the rule of each man. __Answers may include these facts.__
   Guzmán Blanco __established order; built roads and communication systems; foreign firms invested in Venezuela__
   Juan Vicente Gómez __petroleum industry started up; paid National debt; strong army.__
7. When the worldwide demand for petroleum decreased in the early 1980s, Venezuela's economy, based mainly on oil exports, was hit hard. What has the Venezuelan government done to lower the country's economic dependence on oil?

   __production of petrochemicals and liquified petroleum gas; develop aluminum and steel industries__

Culture and People

1. What would you do if you were a *llaneros* in Venezuela?

   __herd cattle - they are cowhands__

2. Venezuela has a population of about __20 million__ people.
3. About __10__ percent of the people live in rural areas and about __90__ percent live in cities and towns.
4. Though it is not the country's official religion, most Venezuelans are __Catholic__.
5. The official language of Venezuela is __Spanish__.
6. The national dish of Venezuela is called __hallaca__. Served mainly at Christmas, it consists of __cornmeal dough__ filled with a variety of foods and cooked in banana leaf wrappers.
7. Write a brief description of the dancing in Venezuela.

   __Descriptions might include salsa, merengue, guaracha, and Joropo.__

8. The most popular spectator sports in Venezuela are __baseball__ and __soccer__.
9. Two famous abstract artists of the 1900s are __Alejandro Otero__ and __Jesús Soto__. Choose one of the artists. Find photographs and information about that artist's work. As an art critic, write about the artist's work and your opinion of it.

   __Answers will vary.__

Cities in Venezuela

Read about the following four cities. Then write three facts about each of them.

Barquisimeto
__Facts will vary.__
1. _____
2. _____
3. _____

Caracas
1. _____
2. _____
3. _____

Ciudad Bolívar
1. _____
2. _____
3. _____

Maracaibo
1. _____
2. _____
3. _____

Name _____

Acrostic Poem

Write a word or phrase about Venezuela using each of the letters in the word Venezuela to make an acrostic poem. Each letter does not have to begin a line of the poem; it can be found anywhere within the line. Draw pictures about the poem around the edge of the paper.

Poems
will
vary.

V
E
N
E
Z
U
E
L
A

Page 97

Name _____

A Letter About Venezuela

You have just spent a week in Venezuela. Write a letter to a friend or relative about the highlights of your trip.

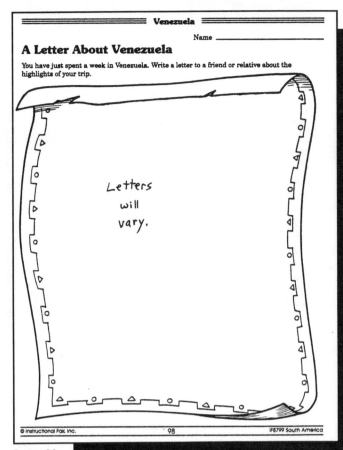

Letters
will
vary.

Page 98

Name _____

Chief Products of Venezuela

List and draw the chief products of Venezuela. If you don't know what something is, consult an encyclopedia or dictionary so you will know how to draw it.

Agriculture:

Answers
will
vary.

Manufacturing:

Mining:

Page 99

Name _____

Map Activity

Make a pictorial map of Venezuela. Draw and color a variety of pictures on the map that relate to the country of Venezuela. These pictures might include animals, plants, crops, places of interest, famous people, etc. Include at least 12 different topics. Include a key on the bottom of your map that explains what your pictures represent.

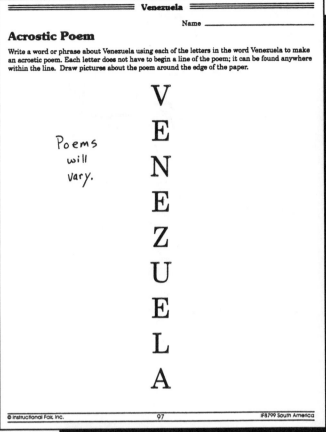

Pictures
will
vary.

Key

Page 100

French Guiana
(gee-AH-nuh or gee-AN-uh)

Name _____

General Information

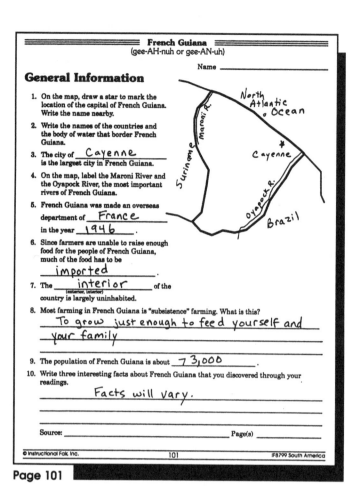

1. On the map, draw a star to mark the location of the capital of French Guiana. Write the name nearby.
2. Write the names of the countries and the body of water that border French Guiana.
3. The city of __Cayenne__ is the largest city in French Guiana.
4. On the map, label the Maroni River and the Oyapock River, the most important rivers of French Guiana.
5. French Guiana was made an overseas department of __France__ in the year __1946__.
6. Since farmers are unable to raise enough food for the people of French Guiana, much of the food has to be __imported__
7. The __interior__ (exterior, interior) of the country is largely uninhabited.
8. Most farming in French Guiana is "subsistence" farming. What is this? __To grow just enough to feed yourself and your family__
9. The population of French Guiana is about __73,000__.
10. Write three interesting facts about French Guiana that you discovered through your readings. __Facts will vary.__

Source: _____ Page(s) _____

© Instructional Fair, Inc. 101 IF8799 South America

Page 101

Falkland Islands
(FAWK-lund)

Name _____

General Information

1. On the map, draw a star to mark the location of the capital of the Falkland Islands. Write the name nearby.
2. The Falkland Islands consist of __two__ large islands and over __200__ smaller islands. Label the larger islands on the map.
3. The islands are located in the __South Atlantic__ Ocean. Color the ocean blue on the map and label it.
4. The population of the Falkland Islands is approximately __2,000__. Most of these people are of __British__ ancestry.
5. Islanders make a living __raising sheep and exporting wool__.
6. The Falkland Islands main source of income comes from __sale of fishing licenses to foreign fishing fleets__.
7. The climate on the islands is __cool and damp__.
8. The Falkland Islands are named after the Englishman __Viscount Falkland__, who was treasurer of the British Navy.
9. Two countries that claim ownership of the FalklandIslands are __Great Britain__ and __Argentina__.
10. In April 1982, __Argentina__ invaded the Falkland Islands, claiming ownership. The British sent troops, ships, and planes. By June 1982, __Argentina__ surrendered.

© Instructional Fair, Inc. 102 IF8799 South America

Page 102

About the Authors . . .

Harriet Kinghorn holds a Bachelor of Science and a Master of Science in Education. She was an elementary teacher in Nebraska and Minnesota school districts, and developed and taught the Enrichment Program in East Grand Forks, Minnesota. Harriet has had numerous items published in educational magazines and presents educational workshops. She has also authored and co-authored many educational books. Harriet was nominated as East Grand Forks "Teacher of the Year" and was honored as one of twelve "Honor Teachers of Minnesota" in 1976. She was awarded the "Doane College Alumni Educator of the Year" award in 1994.

Helen Colella graduated from Jersey City State College. She was an elementary school teacher in New Jersey, and a substitute teacher and religious education teacher in Colorado. Now she lives in Loveland, Colorado, and is a freelance writer and editor. She has published short stories for children and adults.

Diane Fusaro has a Bachelor's Degree from Colorado State University in Journalism and Political Science. After 10 years in the business and library fields, she returned to Colorado College to obtain her Master's Degree in Education. She has taught children and adults of all ages and has co-authored several educational publications.

Project Director/Editor: Rhonda DeWaard   **Editors:** Lisa Hancock, Linda Kimble
Graphic Designer: Pat Geasler